W9-ATI-004

WHOA! NELLIE WHOA!

by

KIRKPATRICK COBB

Artworks By R. H. Scott

Royal Publishing Company

General Book Publishers
7918 Maxwell, Dallas, Texas   75217

Printed in the United States of America

25044

Dedicated to my beloved parents who taught their children the joy of living and the satisfaction of unselfish service, as well as such virtues as industry and integrity.

CONTENTS

Chapter I

GRANDPA JONATHAN

The downpour ceased as abruptly as it had started. No sound was heard save the slosh of the carriage wheels through the puddles and the clop-clop of horses' feet in the mud. An occasional huge drop of rain falling from the overhanging pines on the carriage top broke the rhythmical pattern of the wheels and horses. Suddenly the sun burst through the threatening clouds and bathed the landscape in the fresh beauty of spring.

In the carriage were Grandpa Jonathan, Grandma Belle, their two children, Nettie and Bud and the nursemaid Esta.

The little family rode along in silence for they were all weary from their long journey.

Grandpa Jonathan noticed the horses point their ears down the road, "Either some vehicle is approaching or the team hears the sound of the river already."

"I hope the river is not too high to ford," Grandma Belle answered.

Grandpa Jonathan did not seem to hear.

A sharp rise in the road brought the river into view. The Catawba was at full crest flowing and swirling from bank to bank. As the carriage came closer to the muddy, turbulent water, the team snorted in fear. They stopped at the water's edge. Grandpa Jonathan saw the bay tremble.

"I guess we'll have to swim across this time. The water is the highest I've seen at this shallow ford."

"But Jonathan, this is the worst flood we have ever seen here. Look at the limbs and logs floating down the river. Do you want to drown us?"

Grandpa Jonathan thought seriously for a moment "Belle, this Rockaway carriage was built to ford streams. The body is water-tight as a boat. The heavy wheels will keep it upright under any circumstances. This team of horses I trained myself and both are good swimmers. Your mother's home is only half an hour away and it would take six hours to return home. We've no alternate choice, Belle. We will cross."

Grandma Belle knew that when Grandpa Jonathan made up his mind, further talk was unnecessary. She watched him carefully remove his coat which he handed to her along with his wallet, his watch and valuables from his pants pockets. He yanked off his boots and threw them on the floor of the carriage.

Grandpa Jonathan spoke calmly to the team, " Dick!! Red! Let's go."

Dick started forward at the command, but Red reared on his hind legs. Grandpa Jonathan did not strike him with the whip. He did not wish to take a team of frightened horses across the turbulent river. He jumped to the ground and went to the horses' heads, and taking Red's bridle in his hand he led the team into the swirling water. This team he had raised and trained, and both horses responded as a child in fear does to his mother's leadershsip.

Soon the water was up to Grandpa's waist and then horses and Grandpa were swimming. The carriage was afloat and now they neared the middle of the river.

Grandpa had released his hold on Red's bridle for he knew that Red would follow him anywhere.

No sound came from the occupants of the carriage. The children were enjoying fearfully their voyage on the water. While Grandma Belle seemed to move her lips in prayer, old Esta held her hand over her mouth, sealing her lips.

The force of the water carried carriage, team and Grandpa Jonathan down stream. He swam with powerful strokes urging the team to follow with greater effort. He remembered a logging crossing about a quarter mile down-stream and he hoped to get ashore there.

A carriage wheel hit a sunken rock and the children and old Esta screamed. The carriage was tossed like a tiny boat on a monstrous ocean wave, but the heavy wheels stabilized it at once.

As the carriage passed mid-point of the river Grandma Belle looked up stream and saw a huge log bearing down on them. She fervently prayed that the log would miss their frail craft. The log swept by the rear of the carriage with inches to spare as Grandpa Jonathan urged the team to greater effort.

"Come on Red. Come on Dick. We must get out of here, boys."

Soon they gained the rocky bottom and stumbling over rocks, the team and Grandpa Jonathan struggled up the logging landing. As the carriage reached the safety of land the team stopped, panting, and Grandpa Jonathan sank exhausted on a patch of green grass near the road.

In a few minutes he was on his feet again fully revived. He wrung the water from his trousers and shirt as well as he could and thrust his huge feet into his boots. As he resumed his seat in the carriage Grandma Belle silently wrapped a warm blanket about his wet shoulders.

"Well that was quite a voyage," was Grandpa Jonathan's only comment as they found their way back to the main road.

* * *

Grandpa Jonathan was born on the old Kirkpatrick plantation six miles south of Charlotte, North Carolina, in 1841. When he had finished the common schools, at the age of fourteen years, he entered Steele Academy and completed a three year course. Two of his uncles had founded Erskine College in Due West, South Carolina, so it was natural that he elected to enroll there in 1857 and obtained his A.B. degree three years later.

His uncles wanted him to study law for they felt that he would be highly successful since he was an eloquent speaker, but his mother hoped in her dreams that he would become a preacher. He elected to become an educator.

After graduation from Erskine he accepted a principalship at the Pleasant Hill Academy in Union City, Tennessee, but before the school year was completed war erupted between the North and the South. He helped raise the first company of Confederate volunteers in Western Tennessee and was commissioned a lieutenant. This volunteer group later was reorganized into the Fifth Tennessee Regiment and in June became a part of General Cheatham's Brigade.

His company fought in the battle of Iron Mountain, Missouri, and again at Bellmount in November, 1861. In the battle of Shiloh his company engaged the foe in bitter hand to hand fighting and he was badly wounded in the left hip. The wound was so serious that he suffered seriously for the next ten years and his leg was stiff all his life.

There were no adequate hospitals and because of this wound his commanding officer recommended disability discharge. Grandpa did not want to stop fighting so he protested to his superior, "Don't send me home for just a scratch like this. Even if I'm wounded I'm twice as good a fighter as any other man you have and six times as good as any Yankee we might meet."

The argument was to no avail. "We recognize your worth and your bravery, but you may get a serious infection and lose your leg if you stay here. Go home and get well. In six months you should be able to fight again, if we have not whipped the Yankees by that time."

Reluctantly Grandpa Jonathan returned home limping from his open wound. He was received as a local hero and enjoyed the plaudits of citizenry and friends, but he never ceased scheming to return to the service. Two months after he returned he helped organize a volunteer cavalry company at Charlotte and was re-enlisted.

Because of his unhealed wound, he was not commissioned, in fact the only way he was allowed to enlist was as an orderly sergeant. His major refused at first to allow him to accompany the troop, "Look, you are in no condition to fight yet. Stay home and get your wound healed."

"But the war may be over before then," Grandpa argued, "and I want to fight for the South."

Because of his previous excellent service, the major finally said, "No fighting for you yet. If you feel you must come, we will make you an orderly sergeant."

The following August he was assigned to General Hill

11

in Eastern North Carolina. In the battle of Kingston, December, 1862, he was shot through the left thigh but quickly recovered.

Meanwhile he was re-commissioned and assigned to General Lee in Virginia and participated in the battle of Cedar Mountain, and in the second battle of Manassas, more commonly known as "Bull Run." Still serving as an officer under Robert E. Lee he fought in the battle of Brandy Station and was wounded again in the left leg, this time below the knee.

His regiment took no part in the battle of Gettysburg until the morning of July 5 as Lee began his retreat. Assigned to cover the rear, in fierce hand to hand fighting with sabers, he was unhorsed and knocked senseless, but not seriously hurt.

In the battle of Jackshop, Virginia, he was slightly wounded across the abdomen and his horse was killed and fell across him, pinning him down. He was unable to withdraw his leg and subsequently was taken prisoner and removed to the Federal prison at Point Lookout, Maryland.

One day four of the prisoners came to Grandpa and asked him to preach for them. " I'm no preacher," astonished Grandpa said, "I've been a school teacher and principal."

"Yes, but you speak eloquently and have a vast store of knowledge. Please preach for us. We need it in this lonesome hole," they pled.

Grandpa said he would think about it and the following Sunday preached his first sermon. Thereafter he was to preach almost daily for he saw that the men needed his talks as he preferred to call his sermons.

One night a prisoner, who was to be paroled the next

day, died in his sleep, so Grandpa traded papers with him. The ruse worked perfectly and Grandpa was free.

Immediately he sought the nearest Confederate troops, which were Major William Lee's Scouting Corps. Grandpa was immediately commissioned as captain and assigned to command a company of Scouts.

His company participated in the battle of Wilderness in May, 1864, and then in the engagements at Cold Harbor June 1 to 12. Grandpa took part in thirty skirmishes and engagements in less than a month. In one of these he was buried alive by a shell explosion while lying unhorsed in a ditch. He was rescued and was not badly hurt, but his hearing was permantly affected by the explosion.

One night six Yankee recruits lost their way and stumbled into Grandpa's company camp. The prisoners had been out foraging and had about fifty young chickens in their bags. Grandpa questioned them concerning the location of their troops and where they stole the chickens, but they had been wandering for hours and were so hopelessly lost that Grandpa got no factual information from them. He ordered the prisoners placed under guard and told the company cook to serve the chicken for breakfast.

The prisoners were brought in to eat with the company next morning, but one recruit refused to eat. He seemed disturbed so Grandpa questioned him.

"You can't get me to eat when you are going to shoot me or cut off my ears," sobbed the young recruit.

"Where do you get such ideas that we're going to shoot you or cut off your ears?" Grandpa asked with amusement.

"Last night I asked one of the guards what you did

with your prisoners and he said that's what you did."

Grandpa's roar of laughter rang through the woods. If Yankees had been near they would have trembled in fear or dismay.

"Well, son, we're neither going to shoot you nor cut off your ears, and the guard should not have jokingly said that we were. We'll take you with us today and you may be in prison tonight, but on the other hand we may turn you loose. So eat now for you have to walk some." The lad ate a hearty breakfast. After a two hour walk away from his own troops he was released with his companions.

In the fall of 1864 and winter of 1865 Grandpa's company of Scouts spent most of the time harrassing the rear of General Grant's army in eastern Virginia.

Near the end of February Grandpa and most of his company were captured near Fort Powhatan at the confluence of the James and Appomattox Rivers. Grandpa was taken to Washington and placed with one thousand other Confederate officers in the old Capitol Prison.

The story of the treatment of Confederate officers in this old prison has been recorded elsewhere and need not be repeated here. Suffering from his old wounds and lack of medical care and adequate food, Grandpa's health deteriorated. He always felt that this imprisonment affected his future health more than all his wounds.

Robert E. Lee surrendered at Appomattox in April 1865, and on May 27 Grandpa took the oath of allegiance to the Federal government and made his way home.

Grandpa always felt that the South could have licked Grant if he had not been in prison. The war and his wounds left their marks on Grandpa. For the rest of his life an urge possessed him to push forward, and he continued to live life with the same zest with which he had led his company against Yankee soldiers at the Second Battle of Bull Run.

There was little left of the old plantation. While the slaves were now free, most of them elected to stay and work for Marse Jonathan. But the plantation was badly run down, so in order to support the plantation Grandpa traded in United States Bonds and stocks.

While on a hunting trip into South Carolina, Grandpa again saw his old sweetheart Belle McMillan. She was now the widow Belle Lilly, for during the war she was wooed and won by the handsome Captain Lilly. The captain was killed in battle in 1864 and eighteen months later in November 1865, Belle Lilly became the bride of Grandpa Jonathan and came to Charlotte to live on the old plantation. Grandpa continued to struggle to pay off the bills that had accumulated during the war.

When North Carolina was reconstructed in 1866, Grandpa was elected Justice of the Peace by both parties and two years later they selected him to serve as County Judge. Meantime he began to preach in his local church even though he was not regularly ordained to be a minister until 1874.

Grandpa helped found Polk Academy in Pineville in 1872 and served as principal there. Meanwhile he had sold the old plantation and bought a general store in Pineville. The home he built here contained eight large rooms with a fireplace in every room.

History records little disturbance in Mecklenburg County during the days of the reconstruction. For the most part slaves had been kindly treated by their masters and wanted to stay on the plantations as hired help. Grandpa did admit though that he once joined the Ku

Klux Klan and helped run some northern scalawags out of this peaceful region of the south.

Four children were born to Grandpa Jonathan and Grandma Belle while they lived near Charlotte and at Pineville. The first was a son, Yandall, but he was never known by any other name than Bud. The second child was a lovely little girl whom they named Louisa Jeanette for distant relatives, but they never called her anything but Nettie. Two girls followed, Buena and Bellroy and they were addressed by their true names.

These children were happy little folks for they were adored by their parents who showered them with love and affection. There was also the nurse, old Esta, who was sometimes more like a mother than their own mother. They all dearly loved black old Esta and she cared for them with pride and dignity.

Grandpa was forever reaching out to try something new. He preached regularly every Sunday twice a day and conducted prayer meetings on Wednesday nights. Besides this he ran a general store and was principal of Polk Academy.

One freezing night the store caught fire from an overheated stove. The water pipes were frozen, so the store burned to the ground despite efforts of the volunteer fire department which stood helplessly by.

Grandpa now had only his principalship and his preaching to keep him busy.

About this time he became interested in the great state of Texas and was pleased to receive in the mail a letter inviting him to come to Texas to serve as president of Cedar Grove Institute in Kaufman County. He went to Texas, accepted the offer, and wrote to Grandma to sell the home, to pack up, and move out to join him.

Chapter II

TREK TO TEXAS

Grandma Bell was the pampered only child of a wealthy plantation owner. In her childhood slaves dressed her every morning and brushed her hair. They adored her and waited on her every moment of the day.

One day her mother decided that she was old enough now to learn to do fancy needlework. In order to learn how to use the needle her mother suggested that she practice by darning her father's socks.

"Why, mamma, you wouldn't expect me to darn Papa's dirty old socks. I just don't want to do such nasty work."

Her father overheard her reply. "Belle, you're going to darn those socks, not because they are mine, but because your mother asked you to. You're ten years of age and I think it is about time you learned to do something useful. Most of all you must obey your mother."

She darned all her father's socks thereafter and gradually became skilled with the needlework and drawnwork. Throughout the remainder of her life her most cherished gifts to friends were her dainty hand-hemstitched hankerchiefs.

Old Esta refused to move to Texas with the family despite all the urging by the children and Grandma Belle, "No, Missa Belle, I just can't go to Texas. I'se too old, besides all my relatives live 'round Charlotte. I sure a goin' miss you all. I'se jus' afraid to go to that wil' state o' Texas."

So that settled it. But the tearful parting at the railroad station demonstrated the deep affection of the children for Esta and her love for them. They had presents for her and all the other negro friends who came to see them off. Kisses and hugs were exchanged and finally the family was aboard with cries of, "We'll be back to see you. Good-bye. Good-bye."

The little family was taking its first train ride so Grandma Belle had games for the children to play during the three day trip. When they tired of games they counted cows or horses along the railroad, or watched the scenery rushing by.

Old Esta had packed a huge hamper of food. Endless servings of fried chicken, cold ham, cold biscuits, jams, jellies, cookies and fruit gave the long trip the festive air of one continuous picnic.

The last day of the journey the children became excited about seeing their father, and little Buena marched proudly up and down the aisle shouting at the top of her voice, "Tomorrow I'm going to see my papa."

She was cute and two, so her many new friends smiled indulgently. Proudest was older sister Nettie.

Years afterward Nettie told her own children, "Your Grandma and I learned to cook and keep house at the same time when we moved to Texas. But Grandma knew how to sew and taught me. We missed old Esta greatly, but there was no one to take her place in Texas, so we got along somehow and were a happy family."

One time Grandma called to her, "Nettie, I have a boil between the two big toes on my left foot. I wish

18

you would look at it for I think it is about time to open it."

Nettie looked, "Mama, that isn't a boil. That is a big old fat Texas tick and he's sure enough real ripe and ready to open."

Grandma always smiled indulgently whenever this story was repeated.

Grandma was neither lazy or stupid. She was a well educated woman without the experience in the operation of a home. She missed old Esta who had been her nurse in infancy and her guide and helper after her marriage as long as she lived in North Carolina.

Nettie was only ten years when the family moved to Texas, but she was her mother's helper and assumed most of the responsibilities of the home which she learned rapidly. Like her father she was quick, dynamic and loved the challenge of difficult tasks.

Grandpa bought a ranch and preached almost every Sunday even though he had no regular pulpit. The ranch produced no income for the country dried up from lack of rain.

One night the academy burned to the ground since there was no water to put on the fire. The family was now really destitute for the sole income was Grandpa's meager salary as a saddle-bag missionary preacher. Little Nettie packed his saddle-bags with loving care when he was to be away overnight.

On a trip to a small community, Grandpa found no hotel and sought lodging with a poor but religious couple. For the evening meal the woman served "sow belly", corn-bread with neither butter nor molasses, and wild mustard greens.

"If you are a Christian you will eat it and be grateful,"

19

she announced, "If you are not this is better that you deserve. Will you return thanks, parson?"

Grandpa told that story many times thereafter and always broke into hearty laughter. He enjoyed his own jokes and especially if they were on him.

The dry ranch was sold and the family moved from Prairie to College Mound and later to Egypt. Here in a log cabin in the woods, a young son was born. He was named Jonathan for his father.

As a junior his name was followed by a "jr." and his initials were J. R., so "J. R." became his nickname. An old negro woman not understanding the spelling of his name said once disgustedly, "Jar! Jar! Why they want call that nice boy for an old jug?"

While living in Egypt, Grandma received some clippings from a Charlotte newspaper telling of the death in San Francisco of a wealthy uncle. His will named her as one of two heirs to a considerable estate.

The family was now rich. Grandpa bought a big cattle ranch near Tehuacana. The big house in town he selected for a home was surrounded by trees on a ten acre site. But this house was not suitable for a family in such fine circumstances, so Grandpa added more rooms to make it the most pretentious in town.

A huge round oak table all but filled the dining room. The former owner had to leave it. It was too large to move through the door and the house must have been built around it. Nine feet in diameter, it was crowned with another table measuring six feet across. This top table revolved like a lazy susan.

This arrangement resulted in a change of table etiquitte. No longer was it necessary to say, "Please pass the potatoes." You simply took hold of the upper section of the table and turned it until the potatoes were in front of you. There was advantage in waiting, however, until others were helped for you could see the various kinds of foods pass by. This gave you ample time to determine whether or not you wished to partake lightly or generously of the spinach.

On one occasion when two hired men were permitted to eat with the family, they pulled the table at the same time each desiring the roast beef which was half way between the two. Each pulled in the opposite direction. Stalemate continued for some moments so members of the family were unable to help themselves to anything except the food directly in front of them.

Finally Grandma spoke calmly, "God has given us enough food for all," as she helped herself to the mustard greens.

Both men dropped their hands from the turn-table and then turned it so that the roast beef was in front of Grandma. She never again had to speak to either of these men for they always saw that she had the choicest dish passed to her first.

During the many years of her life gentlemen always respected her wishes. They stood when she entered a room. They helped her off and on trains or carriages, and later into automoblies. She expected their courtesy and she received it.

Before employing a ranch hand, Grandpa always gave the man a meal. He believed that a hearty eater was generally a good worker. Usually he fed his candidate in a restaurant. Once he brought his man to his home to eat with the family.

As the family was seated at the table the man reached for the food. Grandpa, who always said grace before each meal, spoke sharply, "Hold on, we always say something before we eat."

"Say anything you like," was the reply. "You can't turn my stomach."

From the ceiling of the high dining room long strips of tissue paper hung down from a light wheel almost to the table. A string attached to this cluster of papers fastened to the side of the room. While food was served, a servant stood by pulling on the string at regular intervals. This caused the paper strands to move gently back and forth and kept the flies from the food.

Bud, still a teenager, often stood by and admired the lazy susan dining table which permitted food to be passed without the "please pass" query. One day after the noon meal was finished and most of the dishes taken to the kitchen, he demonstrated to a friend just how the table worked.

His playmate asked, "How fast will the turn-table go?"

"Oh, I don't know," replied Bud, "Let's see." He started the table spinning to see how fast it would go.

Away went the cream pitcher stricking the wall and spreading rich, thick cream down to the floor. The sugar bowl flew next mixing sugar with the cream. The fancy silver holder containing the glass bottles and jars holding vinegar and mustard and the other condiments splashed on another wall.

For punishment Bud had to clean up all the mess by himself even though the family now had servants. He never tried to see how fast the table would turn again.

In this big house the family lived royally for they had adequate income now and enjoyed happy times together even though Grandpa was often away preaching in distant places.

In this house they enjoyed for the first time a fancy new dessert called "ambrosia." This dish was made by slicing sweet oranges, a new fruit which they enjoyed in the community for the first time. Over the slices of oranges was spread shredded cocoanut, a new import from a strange foreign land.

Trinity University was located in Tehuacana. Grandpa was first affiliated with this school as an instructor and later became a regent. All six of the children attended this college, or the lower grades connected with this school. Bud was still a teenager and wanted to quit school and be a cowboy on Grandpa's big cattle ranch. Grandpa did not approve, but Bud was so persistent that Grandpa finally gave him permission to work on the ranch. He was too young to know that in later years he would regret that he had left school to be a cowboy.

After graduation from Trinity University, Nettie taught school for a year in Potersville. Grandpa felt that Nettie should have the best education possible and the next year he sent her to Waynesburg College in Pennsylvania in 1887. At the end of the school year, the President of the college wrote Grandma a flowery letter describing Nettie's accomplishments as a student there. Among her new achievements was the ability to speak the German language quite fluently, but most of all the president lauded her achievements as an elocutionist.

In Pennsylvania, Nettie learned the newest and most improved methods of teaching, so she was able to secure a better teaching job in the bigger town of Groesbeck.

About this time Grandpa became interested in Oregon, and was described by his friends as having the "Oregon fever." He finally concluded that he had done Texas about all the good that he could. In the years that he had lived in that state, he had organized fourteen churches which boasted over 2,000 members, and he considered that all of them were now strong enough to work with out his help.

The mail, one day, brought a letter from a church in the town of Lebanon, Oregon, asked him if he would consider moving to Oregon and serving as a pastor there. Here was a chance to learn about the far western state and to satisfy himself that it was a good place to live. So he sold the big cattle ranch and he sold the big home in Tehuacana with the lazy susan dining table. Grandpa went off alone to look over Lebanon, Oregon, and see if it were the kind of community in which he wished to raise his family.

His letter returned swiftly. "Lebanon is a beautiful young city situated on the banks of the sparkling Santiam river. I have already bought land on the river bank for our new home. Please come as soon as possible."

When Nettie moved to Groesbeck Grandpa made arrangements for her to room and board in the home of the County Judge. Judge Cobb had a younger brother, Will, who was a handsome southern gentleman. He not only had passed his bar examinations when he was twenty years of age and now had a lucrative law practice, but he was also editor and publisher of the local newspaper. He occasionally enjoyed dinner in the home of his brother for his Yankee sister-in--law was rated the best cook in town. At this dinner table Nettie and the young lawyer first met.

Soon the young lawyer was enjoying his sister-in-law's cooking more often.

No telephones provided rapid communication in those

days. If Will wished to ask Nettie to take a ride in his smart buggy, he sent a note by messenger.

> Dear Miss Nettie:
> May I call for you at four o'clock
> so that we may take a ride together?
>
> Will

Nettie replied by the same messenger.

> Will:
> I shall be happy to ride with you
> at four.
>
> Nettie

Will wishing to call during the evening would write.

> Dear Miss Nettie:
> May I call on you this evening at
> at 8 P.M.?
>
> Will

The reply was always in the affirmative for it was evident to all their friends that the popular young couple was falling in love.

Romance bloomed beautifully and poignantly, for Grandpa was pressing the family to hurry on out to Oregon. The following Spring Nettie and Will became engaged to be married.

Grandpa became impatient that his family was not ready to move. He wrote to Grandma,

"Your new home on the bank of the Santiam River is now complete. Pack up at once and come on to Oregon."

Grandma wrote in reply, "Nettie has become engaged to this wonderful young man who is the brother of Judge Cobb of Groesbeck and refuses to come to Oregon."

Two weeks later the ultimatum came from Grandpa, "Tell Nettie that she is to come on to Lebanon with you all, or she must get married at once if she is to remain there."

Nettie did not wish to marry yet. She was just eighteen, and she wanted to teach for another year. She had learned a lot about newer teaching methods while she was in Pennsylvania and she wished to try out these ideas in the classroom.

Grandpa was adamant. "Come on out to Oregon with your mother or get married at once," he demanded.

So the young couple set the date, July 5, 1888 for the wedding. Grandpa came all the way back from Oregon traveling eight days by slow passenger train. He performed the wedding rites in the Cumberland Presbyterian Church exquisitely decorated with native dog--woods.

The wedding was one of the social events of the year for the young couple had hundreds of warm friends who were present to wish them a happy married life. The honeymoon was spent in faraway Dallas and Fort Worth. All the people in Groesbeck were delighted that this popular young couple were wed.

Chapter III

TREK TO OREGON

In Lebanon Grandpa preached on Sunday, and the rest of the week he dealt in real estate. He not only bought the acreage on the Santiam River where he built his home, but he also developed five other sub-divisions and built houses. He bought a newspaper which was published by his oldest son Bud for many years. Just to keep busy Grandpa became quite interested in Albany College situated fifteen miles away in a town of the same name. He taught there some, but mostly he was interested in the administration and financing of this school.

When a lovely little girl, Susan Isabella, was born to Nettie and Will, Grandma Belle hurried back to Texas to see her namesake. She persuaded Nettie to accompany her back to Oregon for a short visit so Grandpa could also see his darling little granddaughter.

After the dryness of Central Texas, Lebanon seemed like a lovely park, so Nettie, too, fell in love with this new town. Then her parents tried to persuade her and Will to move to Oregon.

Grandpa wrote Will, "I need you here to help Bud run the newspaper. He is unfamiliar with many aspects of publishing and really needs you as an editor."

Nettie, still in Lebanon, wrote urging Will to move to Lebanon.

So Will sold his law practice and his newspaper in Groesbeck and moved to Oregon, and became editor and publisher of the Lebanon newspaper.

After a year Will decided that he would rather operate his own business and established a publishing house at Albany. Nettie meanwhile was teaching art and elocution for she was highly skilled in these two subjects.

A friend of Grandpa's tried to persuade him to come to Seattle to assist in the development of a big subdivision in Ravenna Park on the shores of beautiful Lake Washington. Grandpa was not interested at first, but when later his friend told him of plans to establish a college for women, Grandpa went to Seattle, for a time travelling back and forth on weekends to continue his preaching in Lebanon.

The college was established and the subdivision was sold rapidly, but the additional work become too much for Grandpa and he gave up his preaching in Lebanon.

A second child was born to Nettie and Will. They named him Jesse in honor of Will's older brother who raised Will after his own parents died in his youth.

Grandpa spent more time in Lebanon now that he had a grandson. Later that same year he accepted a call to preach in Seattle.

In connection with his real estate development, Grandpa became part owner of a milling company in Seattle and he tried to persuade Will to sell his business in Albany and accept a position as office manager. The salary was excellent so Will, Nettie and the two children moved to Seattle. They built a large house near Lake Washington and lived happily amid their new surroundings. Nettie's younger sister Buena lived with them for a year and attended the women's college nearby. Will was sometimes away on business trips travelling as far east as Spokane buying grain and selling mill products.

Bud and Bellroy both married while Grandpa lived in Lebanon and spent the rest of their lives building that community. Grandma Belle was happy there too and wished to stay there, but Grandpa's health was not good and his doctor advised him to move to a drier climate. So he accepted a call to preach in Selma, California in the heart of the San Joaquin Valley. He did not engage in real estate there but spent his full time preaching in his own church and making hundreds of friends as he preached in other churches in the valley.

Shortly before he moved, two sailors in Seattle gave Grandpa a parrot. Polly seemed just an ordinary green bird with yellow head and neck. Her language was dignified and her demands few. But one night the parsonage in Selma caught fire and burned to the ground. Neighbors helped remove furniture and much was saved.

Suddenly the rescuers heard voices yelling and screaming in the burning house, "Hell! Hell! What the hell! Why doesn't some one get me out of this damn place. Damn it! I'm burning up! Get me to hell out of here. Help! Help! Hell! Hell"

Polly was rescued but members of the family were embarrassed by her language.

The milling business suffered a severe slump during the depression and Will and Nettie decided to return to Texas where Will intended to re-enter the practice of law.

While they were packing Jesse got hold of some morphine tablets and they thought he would die. The doctors pumped his stomach and they fed him strong coffee as they prodded him and walked him about for hours to keep him awake. The doctor said that if he ever fell asleep he would never awake.

Chapter IV

BACK TO TEXAS AND ON TO CALIFORNIA

I first opened my eyes and yelled for food on the day after Christmas 1893. I was the third child of a happy family, consisting of Papa Will, Mama Nettie, Big Sis, brother Jesse and me.

We had lots of fun. Papa often took us all for long rides in his carriage although sometimes I got hungry and sleepy before we got home. We played together in our yard sometimes, just the three of us children. Sometimes George, the little son of our negro nurse, played with us.

In a little house in our back yard lived Uncle Ned, an old negro. He worked a little around our yard and made whistles and toys for us. We loved Uncle Ned and did not mind when Mama always gave him the choicest pieces of fried chicken.

Black Mamie our nurse stayed with us at night if Papa and Mama were at some party or meeting. Whenever her husband, Buttin' Dick, thought it was time for her to come home, he butted the side of the house with his head and the whole structure trembled. She went to the door and told him to behave and then let him in for refreshments. He was happiest when Mamie found cold fried chicken for him.

As children we really believed that he butted the side of the house with his head. We also believed stories that when the ice-house wanted a freight car of ice moved, they did not call for a switch engine, they simply asked Buttin' Dick to do it. He could move a car of lumber equally well.

Depending on the season he delivered ice or coal to homes and stores during the day and at all times we stood in awe of his prowess.

Christmas morning all of our little negro friends streamed to our door crying, "Christmas gift." If we first said "Christmas gift," they were supposed to give us a Christmas gift, but we always let them say it first for we already had gifts wrapped for all of them.

Every child received firecrackers and Papa helped us shoot them. Christmas was a happy noisy time.

Many guests came to our home at mealtime and Mama was ready to care for any emergency. One time there was scarcely enough chicken for us all. Papa invited a visiting preacher for our Sunday noon meal. Papa carved the roast chicken beautifully placing all the pieces on a large plate. The plate was passed first to our guest. He was busy talking and instead of helping himself to the choicest pieces, he set the whole plate down in front of him and passed his empty plate back to Papa.

Papa had to scrape the bones to get enough for the family, but the preacher ate all that plate of chicken and told Mama she was a good cook. We decided that maybe preachers did not get enough to eat at home.

A few blocks from our house rose a high water stand-pipe supplying the city with water. Located on a slight knoll it was described as having its feet on the ground and its head in the sky. Once we were without water for a whole day as they drained the standpipe so they could clean it out and paint the exterior. In the late afternoon, Papa took me to see what was going on.

A huge steel plate was unbolted from the side at the base and the mud was cleaned out and thrown in a pile. Inside was a wooden raft which supported bedding and food for the man who was to float to the top. That evening the plate was replaced and water turned into the standpipe.

All the next day we waited for him to appear at the top, but he did not show. We were afraid he was drowned.

Mama said, "Children if you are so worried about the man, why don't you include him in your prayers tonight."

The second morning early he was at the top and we saw him cutting the wire screen and lowering a rope. Soon scaffolding was raised and painters were cleaning and painting the outside of the standpipe.

Sudden illness jolted our happy home for Jesse was stricken with what was then called tuberculosis of the hip joint. The trouble may have come from a dislocation, but he was in bed for a long time and suffered agonies. He made slight gains and then had relapses. As he gained back some of his strength the doctors advised a more healthy climate and the family decided to move to California.

Meanwhile Grandpa's old war wounds were still bothering him in Selma and his physician advised him to move to Southern California. He accepted a call to preach at Downey and bought a whole block in the center of town.

My Aunt Buena described Downey as, "a miserable little old town in those days. Lots of the land covered with dry alkali. The only redeeming feature—it was not

33

too far from Long Beach. Every Monday morning we hitched up the carriage and drove down there, tying our team to the pier and enjoying part of the day at the beach."

Our family decided to move to Downey.

I liked Downey. I liked the oranges and apples which grew abundantly in Grandpa's yard.

Uncle J. R. too was most kind to me, he showed me how to pick a long pumpkin stem and reach down into the cider barrel for a drink of cider. After a few days the cider tasted funny and made me feel funny so I did not like it any more. Grandpa said he was making vinegar.

Grandfather did not actively engage in real estate operations in Downey, but it is reported that he advised many a widow regarding investments during this period. Some of these women later became wealthy because he advised them to invest in property in Long Beach then but a small village along the ocean. He said to them, "Long Beach will be a big city some day. It's a good place to put your money."

We stayed with Grandpa for a short time, long enough for me to get my hand in the gears of a hand wringer attached to a washing machine. In Texas the Negro lady took our washing home to clean and iron so this washing machine, operated by hand and the clothes wringer fascinated me—until my finger was mashed.

Grandpa was annoyed because I was a slow dresser, especially in the morning. He promised me a shiny new red wagon if I would get dressed every morning on time for breakfast. I was on time for a week and I won the wagon. Grandpa was pleased especially, for I was never late to breakfast again.

We moved to Pomona and lived in a hotel while Papa was in San Francisco. I had a bad earache and Mama put smelly onion poultices on my ear. Either the smell or the onion cured me.

While we were in the hotel we watched soldiers going to war marching down the streets to the sound of martial music, but we were sad because one of our small friend's father was killed in the war.

A high wire performer strung a wire near our hotel window and excited the crowd and us by his performances. One morning he set a little oil stove on the wire and scrambled some eggs for his breakfast, throwing the shells down to the street below. He seemed to relish his breakfast.

We moved again back to Downey and lived in a white house across the street from Grandpa's and later we moved to Tulare where we lived for many years.

But before we moved to Tulare, Dewey joined our family.

The Southern California climate performed a miracle for Jesse. Soon he was hopping around on his crutches and going everywhere. Grandpa was proud of Jesse's spunk and rewarded him for his energy and courage by giving him a little puppy.

Admiral Dewey had just won the Battle of Manila Bay so the puppy was appropriately named for the admiral.

Dewey and Jesse were inseparable. No matter what Dewey's preoccupation, he was quick to respond to Jesse's shrill call, "Here Dewey! Here Dewey! Dewey! Dewey! Dewey!"

We had just moved into the white house across the street from Grandpa's apple and orange orchard. Few houses had any inside plumbing but we were the proud possessors of a beautiful white two hole "chick sales."

One day Jesse ran hopping and screaming, "Oh, Mama! Mama! Dewey has fallen down the toilet."

I was sent from the scene, but Big Sis reported that Mama used a rake and a broom in the Operation Dewey. As a result of this mishap, Jesse was forbidden ever again to have Dewey's company when he moved in the direction of the little white house.

Later when we moved from Downey, Dewey was left behind with Grandpa and he grew up to be a serene, sedate old dog in spite of his early mishaps.

Chapter V

WE MOVE TO TULARE

The intoxicating fragrance of spring greeted our arrival in Tulare. As we alighted from the train we could see from the depot sweet smelling locust in full bloom lining the streets and spring roses blushing in the city park. Wild flowers in riotous color in vacant lots—poppies, lupins, bluebells, buttercups, baby blue-eyes, Indian paintbrushes and many others. The strange odor of the Catalpa tree with its odd blossoms and long seed pods. Stately elms furnished deep shade for the wide streets. Lush grass grew in parks and in yards, and every home grew fragrant flowers of many hues and smells. The yards showed loving care and thoughtful planning. The fruit trees in bloom in pink and white and red profusion provided mixed perfume for the heady smell of spring.

What made everything so lovely?

Well, everyone said it was the pure water pumped from deep wells—the purest in the state—we were told. It was so soft one scarcely needed soap to wash hands or laundry. We liked this soft water. The women and girls loved it most for a shampoo—it left their hair soft and shiny.

A traveling salesman told me that he made the mistake of taking a bar of soap into his tub one night. "You know I'd a time getting out of that tub. The water got so slippery and full of suds every time I'd try to put one foot over the side of the tub, I'd slip back. Finally in desperation, I held firmly onto the side and sort of rolled out. They ought to put sandpaper on the bottom of bath tubs in this town."

I did not believe his story—but the water would be awfully slippery if you used too much soap.

In the fall the huge elm trees shed their leaves and they floated to the ground as the frost nipped their cheeks and turned them to yellow, brown, orange and orange red. In just a few days the streets and sidewalks would be covered with a deep golden carpet. We loved to walk through the leaves and hear the music of their rustle. If you were barefooted it was even more fun to kick them aside.

One Saturday Mama and all four children were walking down to the grocery store. We all spread out kicking leaves and having lots of fun, when a man leaned over his front gate and counted, "One, two, three, four. Are there any more?"

He raised his voice on the last word and Mama was indignant for she knew he was making fun of her family. She did not reply, but tossed her head and we all swarmed together in close echelon as we walked on toward the center of town. Mama would not speak to that man for a long time. He finally apologized to her and explained that he was just trying to be funny. In later years we had lots of good laughs over this incident.

Tulare was a beautiful city, but there were also many drawbacks. The streets were not paved nor were there paved sidewalks except in front of the stores in the center of town where the sidewalks were made of wood. From sad experiences I can testify that the splinters were bad.

In the wintertime when it rained, the streets were a sea of mud. In the summertime they were dry and dusty, and the dust settled on curtains, on furniture and on clothes. In fact, it settled on everything, everywhere.

The city tried to keep the dust down and twice a day a sprinkler wagon came by our house to wet the streets. The wagon with its big sprinklers at the back was drawn by two huge bay horses. Every two blocks a high stand-pipe filled the wagon. The pipe was fitted with a short hose and valve so that the wagon could drive under it and the driver need not dismount to fill his wagon.

The team stood patiently as the wagon was being filled. The horses knew that the load would be heavy for the first block, and lighter for the second as the tank emptied rapidly.

On hot summer days all the boys on our street liked to follow closely the sprinkler wagon. If the day were mildly warm we allowed the cooling water to strike our bare feet. If the day were very hot we came closer so that the water struck our knees and thighs. If we got our clothes wet it made no difference because we dried quickly.

The man who drove the water-wagon by our house was the father of two of my friends, and sometimes he gave me a short ride with him high up on the driver's seat atop the tank. He would never let me drive his team, he said I was too young. Anyway it was fun to ride with him.

The ice-wagon which delivered ice to our homes was fun too. Electric or gas refrigerators were unknown and most of our refrigeration was with ice. Many people had a "cooler."

A cooler was constructed of a wooden frame with a solid top and bottom and slat shelves, but with open sides. The top generally was covered with galvanized iron to keep the water off your food. On top was a shallow galvanized pan which covered the top of the cooler. The sides of the cooler were covered with burlap, generally from a burlap grain sack. Narrow strips of woolen cloth saturated with water were placed with one end in the pan on top, and the other end down on the burlap. The gravity flow of the water through the wool slowly siphoned the water out of the pan and down the sides of the cooler. The evaporation of the water on the burlap kept the milk and butter from spoiling and the vegetables fresh.

A cooler was generally kept out on the back porch so water would not leak on the floors and there was greater circulation of air on the porch and more rapid evaporation of the water, which kept the cooler at a lower temperature. We kept our old cooler even after we had an ice refrigerator, for it provided extra space to store vegetables and other perishables.

In town ice was delivered daily to everyone who wished it, or you could go to the ice-house and buy ice. I liked to go to the ice-house for the father of one of my friends was the proprietor. He also carried soft drinks and was generous with them. Mama did not think they were very good for small boys, and she pointed out that my small friend who drank so many, had a poor, pasty complexion. So I did not get to drink much of the carbonated beverages.

In summertime when the ice-wagon stopped, a group of small boys quickly gathered hoping the iceman would throw out some small chunks of ice too small to sell. How those boys would enjoy that ice on a hot day.

The team that pulled the ice-wagon stood patiently as the iceman carried ice into a home. Sometimes during his absence a rascal would get into the truck and throw out a good sized chunk of ice, which would shatter on the ground and all the boys and girls would have a piece. One day some boys in the ice-wagon startled the team and it ran away to the ice-house scattering small boys and big chunks of ice along the street. That put a stop to swiping ice for a long time.

The brown clapboard house which became our first home in Tulare was located on a corner lot over half a mile from the center of the business district. The six room house provided three bedrooms, kitchen, dining room and living room, but no bath. Few homes boasted of bathrooms in this town, but running water was plentiful at the kitchen sink.

Mama, assisted by Big Sis and the rest of us, scrubbed the house carefully and then we moved into our shiny new home. But alas, we discovered there were other tenants— bed bugs.

Mama couldn't imagine where they came from and wondered if we had gotten them on our furniture while it was being shipped from Downey to Tulare. Papa explored the situation in his usual careful manner and discovered that they nested under the wall paper in certain sections of the house.

There were no rapid bug killers at the turn of the century, so we applied kerosene generously and finally rid ourselves of the pests, but our house and our bedsteads smelled of coal oil for months.

Neither Papa nor Mama nor we four children knew

41

anyone in this town to which we had moved, but our neighbors on both sides were wonderful. They called and brought us gifts of fruit and fresh vegetables and milk from their own yards. One lady, I recall with pleasure, brought along a wonderful fresh-baked spicy apple pie. She was always my dear friend thereafter.

We marvelled at the beauty of the oleander trees north of us, but our neghbors told us they were deadly poison and that two little girls died the year before from eating the blossoms.

We arranged to get our milk from a neighbor who kept cows, but later were advised that we could no longer get our milk there. The man explained to me that one cow had "kicked the bucket". I thought that the milk was spilled, but the man explained that the cow had died. Bunny was with me and she explained it to Papa that night, "The cow kicked the bucket and died'."

Papa laughed and explained to her that "kick the bucket" meant that the cow had died.

A huge green grasshopper lit on our back porch one afternoon. We were so excited to see a five inch grass--hopper, that we ran for Mama to come see it. Mama seemed to be pleased, "This is certainly a healthy country that grows such big grasshoppers."

Profusions of lupins, poppies, paintbrushes and a dozen other wildflowers grew on vacant lots and in fields, so every day we would pick new bouquets for Mama. Graciously she accepted our gifts and taught us to arrange them artistically in vases.

Just a block from our house grew a small almond orchard and our first work in Tulare was helping this neighbor harvest his crop. Mama and all four children helped hull the almonds, but I had to spend most of my time keeping little sister Bunny out of mischief so the rest of the folks could get some work done.

It was about a mile to the Paige Ranch office where Papa worked. He had no horse, no bicycle and of course no automobile for there just were not any yet. So Papa walked to his work early every morning and walked the mile back at night. Lots of men walked to work even further in those days. Mama taught us to be extra thoughtful of Papa when he got home at night for we knew he was very tired.

We attended the Baptist church the first year we lived in Tulare. It was about a mile away but we liked the people there. All were friendly, interested in Papa and Mama and all of us children. Some of these people were our very closest friends as long as we lived in Tulare although we later joined another church..

A fine old negro, white haired and benovelent, attended this church. He was one of the two negro men in the town. His family would not go to church, but he was there every Sunday morning and sat in the back by the hot wood stove. He missed a lot of the sermon for often the heat from the fire induced sound slumber, but we all respected him highly for his devotion to church work, and for excellent prayers which he was often called on to give. We were all sure that Brother Lewis walked close to God.

The next year we all united with the Congregational church. Grandfather Jonathan was a Presbyterian minister and Papa and Mama belonged to that denomination, but there was no Presbyterian church in Tulare. Grandfather came up to Tulare and discovered that the

Congregational pastor was an old friend and persuaded us all to transfer our membership to this church.

Papa and Mama worshiped in this church for many years. Papa was at one time superintendent of the church school and Mama often taught Sunday school classes or was a leader in the young people's group. All of our family enjoyed going to church and Sunday school except when the Sunday school teacher told my mother that I was the worst boy in her class.

One Sunday I was leaning back in my chair and it fell over backwards. Unfortunately I fell with it. This caused a great deal of laughter from the other boys in the class. The teacher did not like it much and she was cross with me for quite a few Sundays after that. However, years afterwards we became very good friends and I used to call on her when I was older. She put up with a lot from a bunch of boys whom she didn't understand very well.

The preacher was vigorous and full of gestures when emphasizing the points of his sermons. When he sang high notes he would throw his head back as his mouth opened wide, better to let the sound come out. One late spring Sunday morning, he threw his head back with his mouth wide open just as a fly started across the church. The fly saw this big opening and executed a perfect target. The high note was never hit. It ended in a gurgling sound as the preacher finally overcame the fly and spat it out.

All our family enjoyed music and loved to sing. Sometimes the younger members got the tune but not the words. In church one Sunday we were singing a song "Throw out the Lifeline," but little Bunny was singing something else. I listened carefully. She was singing, "Throw Out the Quinine." She was not acquainted with lifelines but she had to take quinine for fever and she disliked it greatly.

About the time that we joined the Congregational church, one of our Baptist friends said to Papa, "I'm leaving my little home ranch to move toward Visalia on a bigger place I've just bought, and I'm wondering if you wouldn't like to take your young family and live on my ranch. The house is very comfortable, there are berry vines and a good family orchard and plenty of room to keep your horse and perhaps rent pasture to your neighbors. I think I can arrange for you to look after the forty acres to the north so that you can rent this pasture and provide some additional income for yourself."

We talked it over in our family and finally Papa and Mama decided it would be a good place to raise a family. It was only a mile and a half to town and ordinarily half an hour would be plenty of time to drive a horse and buggy into town. We discovered after we had moved that there was also lots of open country to roam and room for other exciting adventures.

New railroads moved into California at the turn of the century. The Sante Fe built a line through the San Joaquin valley connecting our community with Visalia, Fresno and San Francisco in one direction and Hanford, Bakersfield and Los Angeles in the other.

A short independent line connected Tulare with Visalia. The locomotive was low and squat and painted brilliant red and black. The tender carried water and a huge pile of big oak chunks which the fireman fed into the roaring fire box. The whistle blew shrill and high as the little train pulled out of the station snorting smoke and huge cinders from the golden squat funnel. The top of the flaring stack seemed wider than the boiler and almost as wide as the engine itself. How we loved to watch this little engine pull out of the station.

The Southern Pacific extended its line from Goshen, a town north of Tulare, east to Visalia and Exeter and on to Porterville, and west to Hanford and Armona and Coalinga to meet the demands for transportation from the new oil field there.

The competion with Southern Pacific and the Santa Fe was too severe for the little railroad line and to our sorrow it was forced to abandon its run. We felt that we had lost a friend.

Chapter VI

FRONT DOOR TO ADVENTURE

Our door on the Fry Ranch sat fifty yards back from the road. In front on one side grew a huge valley oak. On the other side was an umbrella tree which we loved to climb, and throw down the smelly berries. The branches on the oak tree grew nearly twenty feet from the ground, and the trunk, over three feet in diameter grew straight toward the stars. We couldn't climb the oak but we played many games around its base.

In the spring, Papa borrowed a long ladder and fastened a swing to a friendly bough of the oak, and Bunny and I spent happy hours in the swing while Big Sis and Jesse were at school.

Just inside our front fence was a small irrigation ditch carrying water for our thirsty fields. When the snow melted in the spring, the irrigation ditches were full, but by the middle of summer most of them dried up. While we had water, we enjoyed wading in the shallow stream and occasionally caught a small fish. No matter how small, we would carry it in to Mama and ask her to cook it for supper. Mama always graciously accepted our catch and fried it for our supper. Often there was only a taste.

The road in front of our house was the main road between San Francisco and Los Angeles. It was generally referred to as the "Goshen Road," named for the next town to the north.

The Goshen Road was dusty and dirty during the spring and summer months and well into the fall. In the winter, when the rains came, it was a sea of mud. After the grain was harvested in the summer, crews of men drove hayracks drawn by horses along the road and spread straw over the dust. This helped keep the dust down but the straw lasted only a few weeks. It was ground to dust under the wheels of wagons and carriages. Along this dirty, dusty or muddy road passed the travel of early California, This road was our front door to adventure.

The notorious bandits, Sontag and Evans, were still operating in the hills of the lower San Joaquin valley. Occasionally they came out of hiding and held up a train or robbed a bank, or in a sudden raid they robbed a store to get provisions and ammunition, and as suddenly returned to their mountain hide-out. Everyone around Tulare was talking about Sontag and Evans, and blaming the law enforcement officers for not apprehending them. The exploits of the bandits were the most commonplace topic of conversation.

One day while Bunny and I played in our front yard, a mounted officer rode furiously to the north. Bunny and I ran in to tell Mama that the officer had passed our house on horseback for we felt sure that he was after the famous bandits.

We watched for his return and sure enough about an hour later here he came trotting along. But what a strange way to transport a prisoner.

The prisoner was riding a bicycle with one end of rope fastened around his chest and the other end tied to the officer's saddle. As the horse trotted along raising a dust, the prisoner followed riding his bicycle towed by the rope. Bunny and I were sure that the man on bicycle was either Sontag or Evans, and we rushed into the house again to ask Mama which one it might be.

"No, I don't believe it would be either Sontag or Evans for I think these men always ride horses. This was probably just some poor man who had gotten into trouble with the law and the sheriff is taking him to jail."

"Well, Mama," I asked, "hasn't he done something wicked?"

"Yes," she said, "he probably has, and he will be punished, but I believe it is better for you and me to feel sorry for him rather than condemn him."

That afternoon one of my friends from a neighboring farm came over to play with me. We talked about Sontag and Evans.

My friend said, "My daddy says that Sontag and Evans ought to be tarred and feathered and hung." So we discussed what we would do if we caught Sontag and Evans.

My sister Bunny had a beautiful big rag doll, almost as big as she. Mama had bought the printed cloth and made it for Bunny, and surprised her at Christmas with the present. My friend and I suggested to Bunny that we label this doll "Sontag" and tar and feather and hang him. She did not protest, so we proceeded with the execution.

We could not find any tar but we found a can of grease which was used for wagon axles. We applied this freely all over the doll and then went in search of feathers. We found quite a few hen feathers but they did not stick very well to the grease. Only the small ones obliged. Next we found some string and put it around our victim's neck and hung our bandit from the limb of a peach tree.

After his execution we went about our play, and later in the day when Mama came home, Bunny cried and told her about what we had done to her doll. Mama sent me out into the peach orchard to select a green switch and I got a spanking which I guess I deserved. I thought Bunny ought to have a spanking, too. She did not protest very much when we decided to tar and feather and hang her doll.

Past our front door every day streamed plain and fancy carriages taking folks to town or home again, and wagons drawn by two, four or six horses, hauling wood, grain, or hay. Most of the hay was loose for baled hay was rare in those days. Some of the hay was alfalfa, but more was barley, and occasionally wheat or rye. The alfalfa hay rode the best because it seemed to stick together on the hayrack, but the barley hay was slippery and sometimes a teamster would lose part of his load along the rough roads. If just a little hay fell off, he did not pay any attention but went on his way. If a good portion of the load fell off then he would stop and try to reload. We were always glad to see these small piles of hay fall from the wagon, for if the man did not stop to pick it up, we would go out and throw it over the fence to our horses who seemed to enjoy it more than they did the green pastures.

In the early summer, huge combined harvesters moved by our house going from one grain field to the other. On the road they were pulled by eight to sixteen horses or mules. These huge high monsters occupied the whole road and if they met a wagon it had to get out of the way. The long sickles and the gear which supported them were detached and pulled behind by another team. When these harvesters were in the field, they were pulled by twenty-four to thirty-two horses.

Campers, vacation bound, passed by our front door in covered light spring wagons pulled by a team of horses bound for the mountains or for the seashore. Our friend, Tommy Brown, drove his team and spring wagon one summer to Pismo Beach and the next summer to Yosemite Valley. Each year his family would alternate between the two resorts. They would be gone a month, a week on the road each way and two weeks in the mountains or at the seashore. They stayed at favorite campsites going and coming, which was all a part of their vacation outing.

Sometimes cattle were driven along the road for delivery to the railroad siding in Tulare. More often a flock of two or three thousand sheep would pass our front door. These big herds of stock kicked up big clouds of dry dust which rose high in the still air. We enjoyed hearing the "baa, baa," and seeing the black sheep and the little lambs, and the goats, which were their leaders and the sheepherders and their dogs. But Mama did not like the dust. It settled in the house, on her clothes, in the yard, and even in the shed where our beautiful new surrey was kept.

How we loved to spin along the dusty road in our shiny fringed-top surrey. We drove a single horse. Some of our friends drove two horses, matched teams of bays or sorrels. Some people walked by our front door on the way to work or just looking for work. Others went along the dusty road on bicycles, but most of the individual transportation was horseback. Galloping, trotting, walking, all kinds and sizes of horses passed our front door daily.

Huge loads of fireplace wood creaked by on the way to town for fuel for the next winter. Most of the wood was oak, for great groves of huge valley oak trees grew in the San Joaquin Valley. With saw and ax, men reduced these to sizable chunks to burn in fireplaces, in cookstoves, or in heaters. There were no power saws. All cutting was by hand so good woodsmen kept their saws and axes sharp.

The usual pay for cutting a cord of wood was one dollar and that would include sawing down the tree, trimming the limbs, sawing it into wood lengths, and splitting it into sizeable chunks.

As some of these huge loads of firewood were pulled by our home by patient, plodding teams of horses, Mama would say, "That load of wood represents a lot of work, and it also represents comforting warmth or fire to cook meals for some lucky family."

We had a huge fireplace in which we burned big logs in the winter time. They made our whole house warm. Late at night when the logs were reduced to coals, Papa would cover them with ashes so that in the morning he had hot coals to start a fire. In very cold weather we all came out and dressed by the fireplace. It was the only place in the house that was really warm on cold mornings.

I remember the first automobile that passed by our front door, an Oldsmobile with the curved dash, tiller steering and no windshield. It stopped suddenly just beyond our driveway and both occupants, as well as the cushions, pitched out over the curved dash and into the dusty road. The fall did not seem to hurt them much as they were going slowly. They got up and dusted themselves off and walked around a bit. As they brushed the dust from their dusters, I could see a good reason for motorists wearing dusters.

They put the cushions back in the car and tried to get it started again. Curious, I wandered across the road so I could see everything better. I did not laugh when they pitched over the dash of the car, although it looked funny, for Mama had always taught us never to laugh at other people's misfortune no matter how funny it might seem. I thought of this as I stood nearby and watched the men trying to get the car started.

They cranked and cranked but to no avail. Finally, one of the men asked me, "Do you suppose we could get your Daddy to hitch up a team and pull us back to town?"

I explained that my Papa was not at home and there was no one home except my sister Bunny, and me, and my Mama in the house. So he went in and talked to Mama awhile and finally went to the next farm to ask Mr. Walker to pull him to town.

Mr. Walker hitched a team of bays on the front of the Oldsmobile and sat in the drivers seat with one of the men while the third occupant of the car sat on the rear sloping deck.

As the strange arrangement started towards town, my new friends waved to me and shouted, "Good-by and thank you very much."

"You're welcome," I replied, "come and see us again sometime."

They all laughed, and the strange procession passed out of sight. I decided that maybe I knew what a man in town meant the day before when I heard him yell at an automobile, "Get a horse."

Mr. Walker of course had two horses.

The next spring the road officials decided to oil our dusty roads. First, a team came along with a heavy disk which cut the road bed into loose dirt, and then came a big oil tank drawn by four horses with a spray arrangement on the rear. They sprayed one half of the road and let it dry for several days. Next week, they came out and put oil on the other half of the road. No attempt was made to mix the oil with the dirt although later they did come with a big long plank with a team of horses on each end and try to mix together the oil and the earth. This strange arrangement stopped in front of our house and I heard the driver of one of the teams say to a man passing by that they did not like to get the horses feet in the oil for it was injurious to their hoofs.

After the oil was on both sides of the road, wagons came along and some of the wheels picked up big chunks of oily dirt and carried them along as they bumped along the road. This made big holes in the road and the drivers of these wagons did not like this oil on their wheels or on their horses feet. They swore vile oaths. I guess they were talking about the men who put the oil on the road.

The road was a mess.

The people with fine carriages hated the oil most of all. They always tried to drive off to one side of the road but sometimes this was difficult especially where there were bridges or culverts.

We got fresh oil on our surrey and it was a messy job cleaning it off with kerosene. On Sunday, we got oil on our Sunday clothes. Papa never swore but he said some regular words that sounded almost like cuss words.

The next year they oiled some more roads but they had learned to drill the oil into the dirt and mix it together. As the roads got better, more automobiles came chugging by. I never saw another one stop so suddenly, but I saw lots of them that stopped for some reason or other besides a soft tire. Some of them buzzed by our house so fast they killed some of our chickens.

Chickens are dumb anyway. They would go out into the road to pick up the grain that had fallen from big loads of grain hay. This was cheap food for our chickens but quite a few got killed before we decided it was better to keep them in a pen with a high fence. The chickens had also been going across the road to an orchard to eat the fruit which had fallen from the trees.

Our friends, the Smiths, invited us to help ourselves to the fruit for some varieties grew here which we did not have in our own yard. Fruit was not worth much to sell since everybody had his own orchard, and the Southern Pacific Railroad charged so much to haul fruit out of the valley that it just did not pay to ship it.

The most delicious fruit of all on the Smith place was a plum. We had never tasted anything so good. I asked young Mr. Smith the name of this fruit and he replied, "Prunus Samonus."

I asked him what he meant but he just laughed and said, "That's the name of the fruit."

Bunny said, "I guess that means good prunes." And we all laughed.

South of our house were two acres of blackberries. In the spring when these were ripe, we picked and sold many, and Mama canned quite a few. Bunny was not allowed to eat many because they made her sick. Mama said she did not chew her food very well. Maybe she did not have all of her teeth yet. I remember Papa used to scrape apples for her. He would cut the apple in two pieces and then take the end of a table knife and scrape the apple for her so she would not swallow big chunks and get the stomach ache. Sometimes he would scrape an apple for me if I waited until after Bunny had her fill.

In the spring before the fruit was fully ripe, we would sometimes eat green apples or green cherries and get terrible stomach aches. If the aches were real bad, Mama might give us castor oil. We always liked Castoria or Cascara better. Mama usually gave us baking soda for the stomach aches we got from eating the green fruit.

On the Fry Ranch, we also had a family orchard where grew apples, peaches, pears and apricots. This orchard also provided a fine place for green switches to grow. When I was naughty, Mama would send me into the orchard to get a nice green switch so I could have a good switching. I guess she thought it was good for me to have to pick my own switch. She very seldom used them, however, I suppose she thought it was enough punishment to have to think about how a green switch would hurt on bare legs.

Once when I was sent for a switch, I came back with a very tiny one about nine inches long, and Mama said, "Do you think that was what I sent you for?"

"No, Mama," I replied, "but you are so nice I didn't think you would want to spank me very hard today, even if I have been naughty."

Mama just grabbed me real quick and gave me a big hug and kiss. She held me close so long, I don't know whether she was trying to keep from laughing or crying. She always said it hurt her more than it did me when she had to punish me. Anyway I tried to be awfully good for a long time.

Back of the barn was a big pile of dry manure. One afternoon when one of my friends was visiting, we decided it would be fun to take an old dishpan, which was out in the barnyard, and slide down the barn roof on to this manure pile. We did this for about half an hour and then Bunny came along and she wanted to ride. She was just a girl and we didn't think she ought to, but finally let her take one slide down the barn roof. When she hit the top of the manure pile, she just kept right on rolling. She got hurt and cried and cried, and Mama came out and asked us not to slide into the manure pile any more, but it was fun while we did it.

All the grain threshed in the fields was sewed in big one hundred pound burlap sacks. It was hauled to the warehouse and stored in these sacks until it was shipped or milled. From the mill, we bought for our stock "bran", the rough outer shell of wheat, and "shorts" and "middlings" which were not so coarse as bran. We fed these grain products to our stock. Later on, people started eating them and the cereal companies put them up in fancy packages for human consumption.

We were delighted to go to the barn and get a handful of bran or shorts or middlings to eat. The bran was rather coarse eating, but it was safer to eat because the shorts was almost like flour and if you happen to laugh hard while you were eating it, it might suck up your nose and hurt something fierce.

On the farm in addition to our horses were one or two cows, some calves, pigs and chickens. We had fresh eggs every day and fried chicken at least once a week.

One time Papa bought a hundred baby chicks to raise for fryers. They were in a brooder keeping warm one night when a weasel got into the shed and killed most of them. Weasels are worse than skunks. "Skunks just make a smell and kill for food," my brother Jesse said, "but a weasel is the meanest thing of all. They kill just to kill."

Most of our big pigs we sold to the market but occasionally we would butcher a pig and have lots of fresh pork, home-made sausage and "cracklins." Crisp cracklins were my favorite.

One of my jobs was to cut kindling every night and

bring in enough wood for the kitchen stove and in cold weather chunks for the fireplace and the heaters. There were no paper cartons and everything we bought came in a bag or wooden box or crate or barrel. My job was to split up old boxes or barrels and make kindling for starting fires. We always bought two kinds of wood, fireplace wood in big chunks and smaller wood for use in the kitchen stove and heaters.

Mama was a wonderful cook. She was famous for her fried chicken and hot biscuits of which we all ate copiously. The pies, cakes, doughnuts and her homemade bread brought comfort to our stomachs and happiness to our table.

We never ate a meal at our house without thanking God for all his generous gifts. And all the members of the family were supposed to be at breakfast together on time for this devotion. On Sunday morning, each of us was required to repeat a new verse from the Bible and at least once a week in the evening, Papa or Mama read from the scripture and we had family prayers together.

Our meals were not sanctimonious but were filled with laughter and love. One of the rules of our family was that we never said anything bad about each other or anyone else at the table. I believe Papa and Mama lived by this rule always. Not only at the table but in every moment of their lives.

Rural life changed when we got our country telephone line. True, it was not much compared to modern telephone systems.

The top wire of barbed wire fences was the principle vehicle for transmitting messages. Where the barbed wires did not meet they were wired together with plain wire. When the linesman came to a gate, he nailed a 2x4 rail to each post and strung a wire high enough for buggies and hay wagons to drive under. There was no return wire as every phone was grounded directly.

Four batteries occupied the base of each phone and you cranked for the operator or rang the number of the other ten or fifteen people on your own line.

The big treat of the day came at 8 P.M. every evening. The operator rang ten short rings and everyone took down his receiver and listened to the latest news. This was long before radio or television, and it was a real treat to hear the latest news brought to the telephone office by Western Union wire.

A trip to the store was exciting. Oatmeal, beans, sugar sat around the store in big open burlap or cotton bags. Crackers, apples, cookies were in barrels. Flour was in white cloth bags. The forty-nine pound sack was the most popular. It sold for one dollar. Mama could make a lot of bread and biscuits from a sack of flour.

Dried apples and prunes and peaches were cooked for fruit and pies when we first moved to Tulare. But soon Mama learned to can fresh fruit and we all learned to help her. Fruit was canned in glass jars or in tin cans. For the glass jars we had to have fresh rubbers and the fruit had to be boiling hot and the lids screwed down tight.

The tin cans were sealed with wax. They too, were boiling hot and it was ticklish job to place the covers over the can, put a piece of string in the bottom of the groove, and then pour the hot wax into the groove. When you wished to open the can, you pulled the string and the wax popped out of the groove, then you could pry the lid and enjoy your cooked fruit.

Some of the fruit in cans and some of the fruit in jars spoiled each year because all the air was not shut out.

It was fun helping Mama put up fruit and it was more fun eating the canned fruit during the winter months.

Sometimes when we had a big midday meal on Saturday or Sunday when we had company, we would enjoy a simple meal of bread and milk in the evening. We had plenty of rich milk. None of our milk was pasteurized. We had not heard of such a process. Fresh milk was put into wide, flat pans and over night the rich golden cream rose to the top and was skimmed off with a big spoon. Most of the cream was churned into butter. Sometimes we were allowed to put it on our fruit or cereal. This was a special treat.

In the summer months we made lots of home-made ice cream. Mama mixed the ingredients that went into the ice cream, put in the dasher and placed it in the freezer. Papa, assisted by Jesse and me, would put in a layer of ice and then a layer of salt and so on until the ice cream container was covered, then all you had to do was crank. Sometimes you cranked for half an hour and sometimes it seemed almost an hour. I had a feeling in those days that I did more than my share of cranking, but the delicious ice cream more than made up for the work. We were allowed to eat all we could hold.

Chapter VII

IN SICKNESS AND IN HEALTH

All four of us came down with the measles at the same time—Big Sis, Jesse, Bunny and I, but what a lot of fun we had. Mama made our illness seem just like one grand party. She moved two double beds into a large room so that we were all together She read stories to us when we were tired. She taught us new games and when we felt better we sang songs.

"This is just like having a party all the time," said Big Sis.

"I like this even better than going to school," added Jesse.

Neither Bunny nor I had started to school yet so we did not know how to make a comparison. I thought if school is as much fun as we were having, I certainly wanted to go to school soon.

Jesse lost his voice, but he wrote Mama a note, "Am I going to die?" He loved to talk.

While we were sick, Mama told us that there were a number of children's diseases which we might have. "Besides measles, they are chicken-pox, whooping cough, mumps and variations of common colds. All but the cold you generally have just once and then you are over with them." So we started planning having chicken-pox together.

Chicken-pox did not work out so well as the measles

because Big Sis and Jesse came down with it first and they were almost well and ready to go back to school by the time Bunny and I had it.

Mama was an excellent nurse and gave us more attention than she did when we had the measles. "Just remember," she said, "chicken-pox can make scars if you scratch where it itches. And sometimes these scars may be very deep." Next morning she persuaded Papa to come in and see us before he went to work, and she pointed to a small scar on the left side of his forehead. "This," she said, "happened when Papa had chicken-pox. He somehow or other scratched this particular itching spot and caused this little pit. Now you don't want holes like this on your faces or on your arms, do you?"

We agreed that we didn't want any holes in our faces or arms or any place on our bodies, but it was very hard to keep from scratching. Whenever our itching seemed unbearable, Mama annointed the spots with some kind of salve which made them feel better.

We all had the whooping cough at various times and some of us whooped a great deal and some of us only slightly. Mumps was another thing. Big Sis and Jess had the mumps when I was a very small baby and no one really ever knew whether I had them or not. Bunny and Little Sis had them at different times, but I never found time to have the mumps until years afterward.

Little Bunny was susceptible to colds and every year she had what they called membranous croup. Mama would rub her chest with evil smelling ointments and have her inhale a steaming mixture which I thought should have killed any kind of germs. We did not have any shots to prevent these things and most of the medical treatments simply helped nature wear them out.

One winter, just after we moved to Tulare, Bunny had her worst case of the croup. She coughed day and night and seemed to choke up. Our doctor was a nice young man and we were fond of him. Mama sent for him to come to see what he could do to relieve Bunny. While he was there, she had her worst choking spasm. The doctor asked Mama and Big Sis to leave the room. In a few minutes, he came out on the porch and said to Mama, "I have done everything I can, there is nothing you can do now but to pray."

"You mean you are going to stay out here and let my baby die, telling me that all we can do is pray?" Mama marched right up and looked him squarely in the face. "I believe the good Lord intended us to keep on working as we pray." She turned and marched to Bunny's bedside.

Big Sis told us the details. Bunny's face was blue. Mama said, "She seems to be choking to death."

Mama forced open Bunny's mouth and reached in with her fingers and pulled out a long strand of phlegm. Then she put her finger back in Bunny's throat to see if there were any more phlegm there. Satisfying herself that there was none, she placed her mouth on Bunny's and breathed into Bunny's lungs.

Big Sis said Bunny looked almost black when she and Mama went into the room. But after a few minutes Bunny started breathing again That afternoon she was able to sit up in bed and drink some broth.

While Mama was reviving Bunny, the young doctor stood helplessly by. Mama felt sorry for him but Papa was indignant that a doctor seemed to have so little knowledge. He moved away from town shortly thereafter, and we did not have him again for our physician.

Mama vaccinated all of us against smallpox. Two men died in town in the pest house where they put people who had deadly diseases.

Mama scratched our arms with a sharp needle and squeezed the vaccine into the scratch. Bunny wanted her vaccination on her leg. Her arms were so pretty. That was before ladies and girls showed so much leg.

When we were sick with the measles and, most always when one of us was sick, Mama fixed us a drink which she called eggnog. It consisted of milk, grated nutmeg and cinnamon, sugar and a raw egg. Mama would whip this up with an egg beater to a delicious smooth drink. We were all fond of it, and when we were all sick at once with the measles, Mama spent a lot of her time making eggnog for us.

Mama was a thorough and capable nurse. She nursed all of us individually through serious illnesses. She spent many years nursing Jesse back to health and kept all of us healthy by giving us the proper food and cod liver oil as needed in the winter time.

One Sunday afternoon Mama called us four children together and said, "You boys and girls are such wonderful companions and help each other so much, people in the community comment upon your affection for each other and the fact that you are ready to fight for one another if necessary. This kind of loyalty makes us a strong family.

"Now I've got a secret I want to share with you all this afternoon, which may test your loyalty and demand that you extend your love and affection to another member of the family. We're expecting an addition to our family in a few months. I'm sure that you'll develop the same love and affection for this new member of our family which you now have for each other."

A few questions were asked and a few answers given. Bunny wanted to know whether it was to be a boy or a girl. Mama replied, "God gives us life and only God knows whether it is to be a little brother or a little sister so prepare yourself to accept either."

Later on that afternoon all four of us got together and discussed this upsetting situation. "It seems too bad that we are to have another child in our family," said Big Sis. "Here we are a perfect family, two boys and two girls, why do we want another member?"

"Well," Jess replied, "Mama say's we're going to have another baby so I guess there is nothing much we can do about it. Maybe it will be fun to have a new little brother or little sister in our family."

But we were still upset and discussed this impending event many times. At least we agreed that we would not let the new child know that we had ever discussed the fact that he was unwelcome.

The following November, in our home, Little Sis was born. She was a tiny precious little baby and we all fell in love with her immediately and showered her with our love and attention. As she grew, being older brothers and sisters, we all tried to boss her, but she was an independent small person who stood up against all of us. After she learned to walk, I remember her standing squarely on her two feet and replying, "Mama says I don't have to mind you. You can't boss me."

Perhaps we gave her more attention than she wanted, but we loved her greatly. Many years afterwards she told me that one of her long remembered occasions in her life was one time when she was very small, I picked her up in my arms and said, "Little Sis, I love you."

She was warmly affectionate, quick of wit and naturally she became quite sassy to all four of us.

Every Saturday night all of us had a bath whether we needed one or not. In the summer time when we went swimming almost daily, I could really never see any reason for a bath on Saturday night. But a bath was part of the ritual for our home every Saturday night.

We had no bathtubs on the Fry ranch nor did we have running water. Water we got from a pump on the back porch. Beneath the pump was a wooden trough. No, we did not bathe in the wooden trough. It was not quite large enough for that but it did hold water, and one person could pump to fill it while another was carrying water to the big kitchen.

There was an ordinary rural chick sales in the back yard but that was a very cold place except in the middle of summer, and there was no room there to have a bath. So our bathroom was the middle of the kitchen floor.

First, two large wash boilers, holding about thirty gallons apiece, were placed on the big wood stove. If there were room while supper was being cooked, they were there from five o'clock on. If not, they were placed on the stove immediately after supper was cooked, and a roaring wood fire was built in the fire box. At bath time, a large galvanized wash tub was placed in the middle of the kitchen floor and water was dipped from boilers to wash tub. If the water was too hot then cold water was brought from the pump on the back porch.

Mama would bathe Little Sis and Bunny but the rest of us had to take care of our own baths except

Papa helped lift the hot water from the stove because he did not want anyone scalded. After the children were bathed and in bed, Mama and Papa had their baths in the kitchen.

Sometimes there was not enough water for a fresh bath for everyone, so two or three of us in turn bathed in the same water. We complained sometimes about not getting fresh water, but usually did not object for we were anxious to get it over with.

Few homes around Tulare had bathrooms and inside plumbing. Even after we moved back to town we still used the wash tub for our baths. Finally we installed a hot water heater and a tub—also an indoor toilet. We kept the old chick sales in the back yard for any emergency, just in case the toilet did not function well. And after that we kept it for storage. It was a nicely built outhouse.

What a luxury to have running hot water and a tub for baths. The tub, not much by modern standards, was made of galvanized iron set in a redwood frame. We enjoyed it many years before we replaced it with a porcelain tub. Later we installed a second bath room with all the fittings upstairs.

During this time we acquired our first washing machine. It operated by hand. You pushed a lever back and forth, but it was easier than washing over a washboard in a galvanized tub. We still used a wash tub to rinse the clothes in.

Our family physician lived in the same block and when he became ill his grown daughters always came to Mama to get her to make him take his medicine. She could get him to take it every time. He would always laugh and say, "Just to see you operate is enough medicine to make anybody well."

Sometimes when he would come to see one of us kids who was sick in bed, he would look us over and say to Mama, "Well I don't know why you call me. You have done everything that needs to be done. I think you know more about medicine than I do."

Mama would just smile and he would sit and visit.

Wonder drugs were non-existent and many other medicines were expensive and difficult to obtain. So Mama used a few remedies of her own.

I suffered from an intense earache. The doctor could do nothing for it, so Mama fried a pan full of onions and made a big poultice which was placed on my ear. When it cooled off I got another. It took away the pain but how I hated the smell of fried onions. This earache was recurrent and the onion poultice became a warm but unwelcomed friend. It did the work promptly, but fried onions still give me indigestion. Psychological, I suppose.

Kids have frequent colds and coughs. Mama found the most effective cough remedy was a nasty mixture made of horehound and sugar and some other herbs. We kids thought that the taste of the stuff was enough to make anyone quit coughing. Mama discovered that horehound grew wild so she sent us out to gather it from the fields. We thought that it was terrible to take the medicine, but worse to have to go out and pick it to make into more cough medicine. The medicine tasted so nasty we never coughed unless we had to.

Mama took good care of the health of her own family and helped friends during serious illness. Whenever she learned of serious illness in the homes of the poor,

she would call and offer help and advice. People loved
her for her many kindnesses.

Chapter VIII

PROGRAMS AND ENTERTAINMENT

Mama was a popular entertainer. No, she neither danced nor sang yet she was the most sought after entertainer in Tulare. She was an elocutionist. She learned this art of dramatic expression while attending college in Pennsylvania. With her deep feeling and ability to express emotions, we thought she could undoubtedly have been a great dramatic actress had she chosen that vocation. There was scarcely any entertainment of any kind in Tulare during our early years in that community when Mama did not appear on the program.

Many of her best numbers were deeply emotional and some real tear-jerkers. My favorite was a story about a Texas cowboy and his girl. Unfortunately, the girl rode out on the prairie where the cowboy tended the cattle. Not as a result of her presence, but due to a rapid change in the weather accompanied by lightning and thunder, the cattle stampeded. Dramatically they shot their horses and crouched behind their carcasses in an attempt to escape being trampled to death by thousands of hoofs. Shielding the cowboy's body with her own, Lasca was trampled to death but saved the life of her lover.

Even while Bunny was a very small girl, Mama taught her a number of little pieces to recite for public gatherings. She was a cute curly headed child and everybody applauded vigorously for her, both when she was introduced and when she had completed her number.

Big Sis possessed a lovely voice and sang in many community programs. Neither Jesse nor I were considered dramatic although we did appear in school and Sunday school plays.

Bunny was not so gifted vocally, but at Mama's insistence spent hours practising on the piano so she was able to acquit herself creditably. She excelled in accompanying singing groups.

Little Sis achieved success as a singer and she too, as a small child, entertained friends and many groups.

All of us in our home loved to sing and would gather around the piano often to sing old songs. We had lots of friends in Tulare who also liked to sing and who would come over to our place just for an evening of music. Papa loved the gospel songs and his clear baritone joined in best when we sang his favorites.

The first motion pictures were brought to Tulare about this time. The theater was an improvised lot with temporary walls and the show could not start until after it was dark. The silent pictures were crude and flickering. A single pianist beat out the accompanying rhythm. Some times Bunny substituted for these sound effects.

All of our family enjoyed active church work. We children belonged to the young peoples society which was called the Christian Endeavor and this group had lots of social functions at which we sang and had wonderful times. During the summer months, the various organizations of the church held ice-cream socials on the church lawn. We played games and sang and then bought our dish of ice-cream and cake.

Jesse and I liked to be on the clean-up committees

for all organiations, for in that way we got a lot of extra ice-cream and cake. Although I worked just as hard as Jesse at cleaning up, I never could eat as much ice-cream and cake so I always felt that he got the better of the deal.

In the center of town there were a number of vacant lots, so one of the wealthy merchants decided to develop a park there for the benefit of the community. Linder Park became a popular place for entertainment, and every week, during the summer months, there was a musical program. Most of the talent was local and exceedingly good. Mama and Big Sis and Bunny and Little Sis appeared at times on these programs. Sometimes Big or Little Sis wore special costumes such as Japanese, Chinese or Egyptian that added to the enjoyment of the throngs. I think they liked being on programs.

I never was invited to participate in these programs so joined friends out beyond the seats. We lay on the cool soft grass and visited. After all, I had heard all of my sisters and Mama's numbers at home before I came to the program, but it was wonderful place to meet friends and have an evening of visiting.

Both Big Sis and Little Sis were in programs in elementary school and highschool and in college. Little Sis took the lead in musical comedies. She was an accomplished musician and played a number of musical instruments including the harp. After graduation from high school, Big Sis in Los Angeles studied vocal music under some of the best teachers.

Every year a chautauqua came to Tulare. This program provided a week of speakers, music, dancers and entertainment of all sorts. It was supposed to be very high class. I can not say that I always enjoyed the talks although some of them were very humorous and some of the leading men of our country, such as William Jennings Bryan, spoke from the platform. There were afternoons and evenings of music, all excellent. We were privileged to hear musical groups from many foreign lands and learned a lot about the world. There were also peanuts and popcorn and pink lemonade which we all enjoyed. The hamburger and the hot dog had not reached their peak of popularity.

People for miles around hitched their teams to their fanciest carriages and rode into the Chautauqua. They tied the teams to the tie-racks around the chautauqua grounds. Most owners unhitched their teams and fed them for they were going to spend all day waiting while their masters attended the chautauqua.

The chautauquas were held in tents and the afternoon meetings got very warm so they put up the sides of the tent to let the air go through.

One hot dry evening during a serious talk there was a sound like the patter of rain on the top of the tent. Two men near the door rushed out and apprehended two of my friends. They had been throwing corn on the roof of the tent and as it rolled down it sounded like rain drops.

Papa was one of the sponsors for the chautauqua for he believed good citizens should share in bringing cultural programs to a community.

Once a year the circus with its accompanying parade came to town. It moved in during the night and in the early morning hours the animals and all the paraphernalia were removed from the flat cars.

Some of my friends went to the circus lot to carry water for elephants and do other chores so that they could get free tickets to get into the circus. Mama did not approve of this so I never was permitted to water the elephants although one time I helped one of my friends carry water. Elephants drink an awful lot of water. I would rather earn my admission to the circus some other way.

Papa would generally take us to the circus. We would arrive early at my insistence and Papa would sit patiently through the whole performance to the very end. I never knew whether or not he enjoyed it until I had children of my own and took them to circuses. I found children a good excuse for seeing a circus again.

Most of all we loved the parade with the big animals and the tigers and lions and bears in their cages. The streets would be lined with open-mouthed children and their indulgent parents as these unfamiliar animals paraded down the streets of our town.

Our house in Tulare was a center of active social life. If there were no party scheduled for Friday, then my sister, Bunny, would plan that we would have a party at home and invite in all of our best friends. These were uproarious happy times. Sometimes we played group games such as charades, spin-the-platter, and occasionally, a game called post-office which involved the right to kiss on certain occasions. Mama did not particularly care for this game and so we did not play it so often as the others.

Then there were all types of card games such as Flinch, Pit and Authors. My brother, Jesse, was always the most vociferous player and he generally won. We were very proud of him although sometimes he irked us tremendously.

One time at our house, we held a big party of church friends and among the guests was a newcomer from England. Our family was very fond of Spanish food and there was a woman in our town who made delicious tamales—plump with chicken and plenty of good Spanish cornmeal. The tamales she made were not only delicious but large enough to be a whole meal. We were all sitting around tables in our home taking the husks off our tamales when I looked up and saw this Englishman.

"How do you like tamales?" I asked him.

"Oh," he said, "I've never eaten one. I really don't know."

By this time I had the shucks removed from my tamale and placed in the big platter which Mama had provided for shucks in the middle of each table. The Englishman was still toying with his tamale. I was ready to eat mine and wished he would hurry so we could all start together. Mama always told us to wait for other people.

"These are very good chicken tamales," I explained, "they are made by Mrs. Valencia, who is the best tamale maker in these parts."

I pointed to my tamale and said, "See how much chicken there is in this tamale?"

My friend had ceased to pull his tamale apart. I noticed he was beginning to put the shucks back around the tamale.

"What's the matter?" I asked. "Don't you like tamales?"

He replied, "Oh, I'm afraid the chicken will get out."

Mama came along at that time and she seemed to understand him better than I, because she brought him some other food. Although he sang in our church choir

76

for years, I was never able to understand why he didn't like tamales.

The hobo stew was another one of our favorite parties. Often we would get someone with a hayrack and team to haul us to some nearby park or some sandy creek bank where we would cook our own meal. This might be a regular stew which we made on the spot in an old five gallon oil can or it might be corn cooked in the shucks on the cob in the coals and ashes of a fire. There was never any better food than this.

Jesse and I were generally assigned the job of making the coffee which was also made in a big five gallon oil can over another fire. One time we were so busy playing with other young people that we forgot to watch the coffee and it all boiled down. In fact, there was just a half inch of water in the five gallon can when we came back from our play. The coffee looked awfully black and thick, but we filled it up with water and everybody drank it and said it was good. I was not allowed to drink coffee at that age so I really wouldn't know.

There were few automobiles ,and they were not dependable. but a hayride was a pleasant and enjoyable means of transportation to a party or picnic. Nothing was on the road at night to interfere with a wagon except an occasional passing wagon or carriage, so the hayride was our most important means of transportation to parties out of town. We had so many farmer friends in our church and community, it was never difficult to get such a ride.

Generally, the hayrack would be loaded with fresh hay about a foot thick on the bed of the rack, and we would sit around the sides with our backs to the sides of the rack which generally leaned outward. We had lots of fun singing songs as we went back and forth to our parties.

For a Senior Class picnic in our high school we enjoyed a hayride to Rocky Hill near Exeter twenty miles away from our school. Four horses were hitched to the hayrack and we all piled into this one rack. There were not more than thirty people in the whole group including our chaperons, and it really was a long drive—four or five hours. But we had a good time at Rocky Hill exploring and eating a tremendous meal late in the afternoon. We ate another cold supper and started our ride back in the moonlight. Seniors in high school are a little sentimental and I have always felt that a few of the marriages that resulted from our high school association originated on that evening.

While I was in college, I learned to play the ukelele and thereafter was very popular on hayrides which by this time had become a novelty rather than a means of transportation back and forth. Hayrides, I understand, are still popular in Tulare, but generally a rubber-tired tractor pulls the wagon rather than a team of horses.

Between our house and the main part of town were the railroad tracks. At one time, Tulare was a railroad center for the Southern Pacific railroad and there were still lots of tracks to be crossed. Mama didn't care for us to loiter along the railroad tracks because she knew that there were sometimes undesirable people thereabout. Sometimes long freight trains would block our route and we would either have to climb over or under while some companion watched to see if the locomotive had attached itself to the freight cars. I never rode any freight trains since Mama and Papa both objected strenuously.

As soon as school was dismissed for summer some boys went to the railroad station to sell apricots and other early fruit to the passengers through the open car windows. I was never allowed to sell fruit for my parents did not believe that small boys should be hanging around railroad stations, but sometimes on the way home from an errand down-town I watched the other boys. They sold their bags of fruit for a nickel and some did quite well.

One boy who was not so bright could not move fast enough to make many sales, started to sell his fruit two bags for a nickel. Then the fun commenced.

As soon as the train pulled out, the other boys jumped the two-for-a-nickel fellow. He ran and they were so angry they started throwing apricots at him as he fled. His home was beyond our place and he ran into our yard. I felt sorry for him for his back was all covered with splattered apricots.

After that lots of boys picked on him. They were mad because some of the apricots thrown at the boy splashed over the depot and the railroad agent prohibited fruit sales thereafter. The boys blamed the cut-rate salesman for their difficulty.

Chapter IX

WE GO TO SCHOOL

Grandpa, annoyed that I was so timid and quiet, tried to help me gain self-assurance. He said, "Don't take anything off of anyone, just remember that you can lick anybody if you make up your mind to do it."

When I started to school I had at least one fight a day. Some bully would come up to me and ask if I wanted to fight. Grandpa should have been proud of me, I always said "Yes."

My opponent would place a chip on his shoulder and say, "All right, knock that chip off my shoulder."

I knocked the chip off.

Grandpa taught me that I ought to be ready to fight, but he did not teach me how to fight, so generally these fights did not last long. My more skilled opponent hit me squarely on the nose and the blood started to flow. Both the opponent and I decided about the same time that I was licked. And I guess I was. I had to learn the hard way.

At home I had been taught never to fight Jesse because he was crippled, but somehow or other he always got the best of me. Grandpa simply was trying to teach me to take bullying from nobody, and although I could not fight, at least I was respected as being one who was willing. Consequently, many larger boys challenged me to fistic encounter. I learned rapidly and finally flattened a boy much larger than myself. After that boys did not invite me to fight.

Teachers did not seem to care if we had fights as long as we were off the school ground, but I got one black eye on the school ground when I was not even fighting.

Each member of our class was given a small plot on which to plant a garden. I planted radishes, carrots and lettuce. One day while I was tending my garden a boy yelled at me through a high board fence. I peeked through the knothole to see what he wanted and just at that moment he rammed a big stick through the hole and I had a black eye. Worst part was I did not get to see the boy, so did not know who fixed my eye.

Mama came to school to learn how I got the black eye and she also learned that I had been fighting after school. She asked me why I wanted to fight and I told her about Grandpa.

"I think," she said, weighing each word, "your Grandpa meant that you should be ready to fight for a worthy cause rather than just fighting to lick somebody."

She asked me not to fight anymore unless it was necessary.

Big Sis enrolled in a different school from the one I attended and Jesse in still a third school. Most of this fighting occurred on the way over to the other school where I had to wait for Jesse who was dismissesd at a later hour. As soon as he came out, we would hitch up our horse to the buggy and drive around to pick up Big Sis and be on our way home. Once as I was waiting for Jesse to come out of his school, some big boys came along and tried to pick a fight with me. I did not want to fight but defended myself as best I could. Just then Big

Sis, dismissed early, came up. She tore into the bullies and stopped them in a hurry.

There was little supervision on the school ground, and some kids were always getting into fights. Sometimes they would just be wrestling and then someone would get angry and fists would start flying.

Sometimes we got into trouble without trying. One day we were chasing a football and it got loose and bounced across the street with a lot of us after it. We got pushed into a fence and knocked down about twenty feet of it. The owner came out and he really told us, and we were in trouble with the school principal.

I remember one boy called Kalamazoo was out in the country with some other boys on a Saturday. Becoming separated from his friends, he climbed a pole to see where the other boys were. He threw one arm over a wire and grabbed another wire with his hands. He was electrocuted they said. They amputated his left arm, leaving just a stub below his shoulder and on his other hand, they cut off all of his four fingers and the first joint of his thumb. This impressed me greatly for this boy sat in front of me at school and I was directed to help him. I used to put rubber bands around the stub of his hand and thumb to hold his pencil or pen, and he learned to write beautifully with this stub hand which was drawn in at right angles to his forearm. He could draw better than anyone in our class. He was a superior student.

One day he got into a heated argument with a bigger boy and wanted to fight him. The other boy did not want to fight him and we tried to dissuade him. That noon they all went off the school ground a couple of blocks and really had a fight.

This one armed chap with his crippled hand and a little

short stub on his left side, could hit three times as fast and apparently twice as hard as his bigger opponent, who soon had a bloody mess for a nose and face. The bigger boy was down and ready to give up but his opponent would not quit when the principal arrived. No one ever offered to fight Kalamazoo again.

In the main grammar school I attended, the boys were on one side of the high two story building and the girls were on the other. We marched in and out of class that way and that was the way we played—a high board wooden fence separated us.

Some of the boys shot darts made from shingles at the big four-faced clock atop the building. Each used a long piece of bamboo with a string fastened at one end. A loop tied in the other end of the string was hooked into a notch near the pointed heavy end of the shingle dart. The boys tried to stop the clock by sticking these darts in its face. Most of the shots were misses, but fortunately none of the darts hit any girls on the other side of the building.

The dart shooters finally got enough darts in the face of the clock to stop it. That stopped the business of shooting at the clock.

I guess we learned quite a lot at this school. It was an old-fashioned school with children all seated in rows. We generally took school work home for we were expected to study at home in order to do our best work at school. There were some dumb kids in the class—people unable to do the work. I remember that I caught up with several sub-normal people who had been in Big Sis's class and then in Jesse's, and I guess some of them stayed in school so long that they were in the same classes with Bunny later on.

Mama often came to visit school when I was in the first grade. I guess she visited the other rooms too where my sisters and brothers attended but I did not know so much about them. As far as the first grade was concerned, I was always a little embarrassed for she generally found me standing in a corner. Teacher had put me there because I wanted to talk to other pupils about my lessons and the teacher did not tolerate that. Mama told the teacher if I ever got a licking at school, I would get another at home, so that may have been the reason the teacher put me in the corner instead of giving me a licking.

The only whipping I ever got in the school was in the fourth grade. One of the girls had a big mastiff who used to follow her to school and the teacher would allow the dog to come into the class room. He was very quiet. The girl's father was influential in the community and she was also very pretty, and all the boys and girls liked her. She was my girl friend for quite a while. I used to put notes in the corner of her yard on the way to school, telling her how beautiful she was even when I was in the first grade.

Well, we had a visitor in the class and the dog must have been acquainted with the visitor because he stood up on his hind legs and put his forepaws on her shoulder and kissed her right in the face. The lady was so surprised and embarrassed that she fell over backwards and some of us laughed out loud. It really was funny, but the teacher kept those of us she felt had laughed the loudest in after school and spanked our hands with a ruler. I told Mama about it when I got home, but she never spanked me. I guess she thought it was funny too.

In this same fourth grade located in a store building

clear across town from the main school building, I guess they did not have enough rooms in those days either, and were trying to keep off double session, we did not have much playground and the swings were the most popular apparatus.

One day one of my friends was teasing a girl who was swinging and she kicked him in the head and made a lump as big as an egg. We took the boy to the teacher and told her the girl kicked him. The teacher was awful mad when she learned the full story and she wanted to spank them both, but she was so scared about the lump on my friend's head that she did not do anything to either.

After I got promoted over to the big building, I learned a lot of poetry in fact I learned more than anyone else in school. Most of it learned after school. I had to stay in for some minor infraction. Maybe it was because the teachers all knew that Mama would give me a whipping at home if I got one at school so they kept me in and permitted me to learn poetry to improve my mind. I am glad I learned all that poetry. They were worthwhile poems and I knew more than all the rest of the kids in our room put together. If it was so good why do you suppose they did not teach it during the school hours instead of after school.

Now do not get the idea that I was entirely dumb and had to stay after school. We did not hear so much about bright students in those times. Maybe they did not know so much about the difference in people, but you had to pass the work to go on to the next grade and I did skip a couple of grades while attending grammar school. My teacher told Mama I was the best speller in school, and I did spell down all the seventh and eighth grades. I think the final word which no one else could spell was "pomegranate." I hope it is spelled correctly here.

When I was in the seventh grade, once a week I was allowed to go to a class called "sloyd." They call it wood-shop nowadays.

My first assignment in that class was to square a board. The teacher handed me a piece of wood four or five inches wide and about a foot long and told me to square the corners. I planed away on this project week after week. The board got smaller and smaller, but no squarer. Finally it was too small to tell whether it was square or not. I was graduated from that project and allowed to proceed with some other small project which turned out to be more useful.

Mama recognized my frustration in not being able to square a board. She saw that I was supplied with hammer and nails and a saw to work at home. I built many useful things for her including bookcases which were used in our living room for years and she was proud of them as was I. She had a particular understanding of the needs of her children and of the needs of other children. She always kept hammer and nails on hand for small boys who came to visit her. She knew that was an awfully good way to keep small boys out of mischief.

Meanwhile, Jesse and Big Sis had gone to high school. High school was on the same ground as the seventh and eighth grade school I attended. I was very proud to have a big sister and a big brother in high school, and I used to point them out to my friends with pride.

Finally I was promoted into high school with due cere-mony and a grammar school diploma.

I was exposed to a number of high school subjects including history and Latin, algebra and something else, but most I was impressed by Latin. My elementary school had failed to teach me any of the fundamentals of English grammar. I failed Latin the first quarter completely. I was able to master the "amo," "amas," "amat," but for the more complex parts of the pluperfect and the other forms of grammar, I was at a complete loss.

The principal of the high school taught freshman Latin. I felt hopelessly at his mercy, but Big Sis came to my rescue. Just what she told him, I shall never know. However, things improved for me greatly thereafter. At least I lost my fear and was able finally to master the subject with a B average for the year.

The next year we liked Latin. The school employed a cute little Latin teacher, and Latin was the most popular subject in high school. I was tempted, at the end of the second year, to enroll for a third year, but the cute teacher married and so I lost the incentive.

Study hall was one of the things I remember well about that freshman year. It was located on the second floor and the foundations, or something below it, were not too stable. A lot of the boys would place their toes on the floor with heels up and in unison shake their legs up and down. This caused the floor to vibrate up and down, and people all about would look up apprehensively. The nice old commercial teacher in charge of our study hall, would leave his seat up on the platform in front and walk around the room quietly encouraging us to continue with our studies. As soon as he returned to the platform again, we would often resume the same operation and cause him to leave his seat again. This might continue a number of times until he finally decided that he had better remain in the rear of the study hall. This movement on his part promoted more attention to books.

In the second semester, we moved into a new high school across town and we could not shake the floor anymore, but we did manage to have a lot of fun in study hall. It was larger and you might be fortunate to be further away from the teacher in charge if he continued to sit up in front on the platform.

I never knew just how much studying went on in the study hall, but we had to study at home. Mama and Papa insisted on that. Monday, Tuesday, Wednesday, Thursday and sometimes even Sunday night there were books to get at and lessons to be learned. No wonder we had such good grades with so much encouragement at home.

While I was in high school, a boy in another school was killed playing football. So all the high schools around us quit playing American football.

Next year they decided to play Rugby.

Rugby was a new game in California. Supposedly it was less deadly than tackle football. I was permitted to go out for practice with an understanding that I was not to play with other towns. I do not recall that I was a spectacular player. I played "forward," was skinny and wiry, and was able to handle the ball fairly well with my feet. Only the backs were permitted to pick up the ball and run with it or make rugby passes.

At any rate, I became so proficient in the game that I was prevailed upon to play against our rival schools. I was told that I was not patriotic and loyal if I did not play. Mama had already told me that I could not play in other towns, so I didn't ask her, I very foolishly sneaked away to play.

When I came home she was at the front gate to meet me. "Did you get hurt?" she asked.

"No, Mama," I said.

"I'm sorry you did't ask me, son, before you left."

"Yes, Mama." I was ashamed.

She consented for me to play in all the remaining games, but I never did learn how she knew so soon that I played in that first game.

Basketball is a wonderful non-contact sport depending on skill but it used to be different. I played center. I was tall and skinny and not fully developed. Once when our picture was taken, the basketball coach said to me, "Put your fists under your arms so it will look as though you have a little muscle in them." Which I did. I sure looked funny.

I never did get hurt much in football, but I certainly got banged around in basketball, for in those days it was a rough contact game. Because I was tall, I played center and I was able to get my share of baskets. After every score the ball went back to center for a jump ball, and everytime there was a time out, or anything else it went back to center. So the center really had to jump.

One time a new boy came into our league to play center on another team. He had his training in San Francisco. The first four or five times we jumped for the ball, he gave me the shoulder and I was knocked flat on my back. I learned some tricks from him so that I was able to hold my own. Neither he nor I were ever called for fouls for these skillful tactics.

We did not win the league championship that year. The team on which this opponent played won, but we thought we could beat them if we had a chance to play them again because we were greatly improved by the end of the season, and that was the only team that defeated us.

About the middle of April my brother Jesse, who was manager of the basketball team, received a phone call from this other town. They were having a May Day celebration and they wanted to match these two basketball teams again as a special attraction. We were to play in the daytime on a Friday, a school day for us but a holiday in the other community.

Jesse asked the school principal for permission for us to go on the trip. The principal gave him a cold stare and a lecture on suggesting such a thing, so we had a meeting and decided to go anyway.

This was not in keeping with the best tradition of the school, nor was it in keeping with the best tradition of our family, so we did not discuss the problem with Papa and Mama.

Jesse managed to get a truck to take us over, so we went. We lost the game by a close margin.

When we returned to school Monday morning, the principal called us all in to his office and told us we were expelled for two weeks.

We hung around the school as much as we could. They were building some new classrooms and we climbed in and out of those to see how they were getting along.

We had a hard time explaining our expulsion to our parents. I know Jesse took most of the blame for it because he was the manager and I was just a player. I appreciated that too. The boys in other families were prominent in the town, too, and that may have been the reason we were all readmitted to the school a day or two before our two weeks were up. We had a feeling for awhile, however, that we were never to be allowed to return to school and we were very glad when we were re-admitted to our classes.

My, we had a lot of work to make up. I never knew how much people learned in two weeks before.

Jesse and Big Sis graduated from high school that year.

We had a wonderful place for school graduations. There was an old pavilion in the middle of a block between the high school and the town. The graduating class sat on the high platform at one end, and the other classes were located in the balconies, one in the left balcony, one in the center, and one on the right balcony. The freshman sat in the central balcony, which was the furthest from the stage while the other two classes occupied the other positions of greater honor.

The pavilion was beautifully decorated for the occasion. Then the various classes would rig up their class banners on wires and pulleys and run them back and forth down toward the center of the stage. They assembled in the pavilion long before the commencement exercises started and gave their class cheers and songs as they gaily ran their pennants and banners back and forth toward the stage. When the commencement program started all banners were hauled back to classes and there was proper decorum for the remainder of the evening.

With so many boys climbing around up on the rafters in the top of that pavilion it was amazing that someone did not fall and get hurt. As far as I know, no one ever fell out of the rafters.

We were all disappointed when years later the old building was condemned and torn down.

In my senior year, I felt I had acquired some status as an athlete. Jesse, in spite of his short leg, was the best tennis player in school, and his chum, Joe, was the next best player. We had played tennis so much at home and at school, and Jesse had coached me so well that when he and his friend had graduated, I was the best tennis player in school, ready to represent our high school in all events. I continued to play football and basketball, and took an active part in track, all this with the permission of my parents.

I decided the previous summer that I wanted to go into the dairy business. Papa had secured a farm near town for me to start this business venture. I worked hard at it and still did fairly well in school. I also felt that I did fairly well in the farming adventure and made quite a little money, but Papa felt that it was an undue financial burden on him, and at the close of one year, we closed out the dairy farming deal and moved back to town.

While we lived on the farm Big Sis was married in a beautiful outdoor ceremony held under the sweeping palm trees. We were all happy about this first marriage in our family for we were fond of Ralph.

In spite of all my senior year activities, I remember I was pleased when the principal called me into his office and said to me, "Congratulations, I like to see a man like you who can take part in athletics, play football, sing in the glee club, do all the other things you do and still get all A's."

I didn't even know I was getting all A's until I got my report card the next week.

I smiled and thanked him, and told him I did not know that I could keep up getting all A's, but he said, "I'm sure you can."

But I didn't, I got two B's the next quarter.

High school was a mile from our home, and grade school a little over half a mile. Mama expected us home for lunch for there was no cafeteria. She always had a hot lunch waiting for us. I know the walk home was good for us. The hot lunch and Mama's encouragement was even better. This was our routine all the four years I attended high school. We walked home, we enjoyed a good lunch which was always ready. The exercise and the lunch helped us do better school work.

While I was in high school, we had no physical education classes and supervision of athletics was poor. One time as we started a football game in another community, we discovered that the fullback had a few drinks too many. He said he saw at least two balls and he did not know which one to fall on.

Well, we lost the game, the fullback got vacation from school for the rest of the year. Even if we did not have good supervision, they just did not permit players to drink.

Another time the track team went to another community for a dual track meet. I was ill and unable to go. I suppose it was just as well for after the track meet some of the boys got hold of some beer. Some of them drank enough so they were affected when they got on the train to come home.

The principal called them all in to his office. One of my friends said he did not drink any, he just smelled it. He got off with that story, but it was quite a joke around the school for the rest of the year.

Mama wanted us all to go to college, that was her chief interest and her hope, she talked about it for years before we graduated.

Big Sis had not been very well and stayed out of high

school for a year while she visited Grandma and studied music in Los Angeles. The result was that she and Jesse graduated the same year. After graduation Big Sis went to Los Angeles again and stayed with Grandma while she studied vocal music. Sis had a beautiful voice and Los Angeles offered opportunity for advanced training.

After graduation, Jesse stayed out of school and worked. He had become a good finish carpenter and always could get a job in Tulare. He saved his money for his college education.

I finally graduated from high school in 1912 and went to work in a creamery. That fall Jesse enrolled in Pomona College. I worked for six months in the creamery to get enough money to join Jesse the second term. Until his graduation in 1916, I was generally referred to as Ty Cobb's brother. "Ty" was Jesse's nick name at Pomona.

All our friends recognized the family spirit which Mama had helped develop. Jesse helped me get both jobs and advantage at college. He could not get me in the glee club, I just did not have enough training for that, but he did help me get into a drama club, and he helped me in many other ways.

Because of his newspaper experience, Jesse was able to get work with the local paper. He supplemented his college costs by waiting tables and washing dishes and soliciting advertisements for various school publications. I was more apt at janitor and garden work and waiting tables. But because my brother had worked in the advertising department on papers and periodicals, in my junior year I asked for this job also. Temperamentally, I was not suited for it and I can remember many a time, walking around the block before I could screw up enough courage to go in and solicit an ad.

I became interested in selling. I sold magazines. I sold aluminum ware and books, and model T Fords to get through college.

After my junior year I stayed out of school a year and sold Fords. I wanted the experience and I decided to help sister Bunny get started in college.

Chapter X

DOGS, HORSES AND PETS

After so much fun with Dewey, we children felt we could not get along without a dog, so after we moved to Tulare, we begged Papa and Mama for a new pet. In answer to our pleas one of our new friends gave us a white and spotted Irish Terrier. We named him Sport.

Sport was everywhere with Jesse and me on the farm, in pursuit of adventure, swimming, chasing rabbits, squirrels, cats and even chickens if not restrained. He was fun on every occasion, always ready for a frolic, and we taught him many tricks. His love for adventure resulted in his early demise.

A new enemy began to chug along the dusty highway in front of our home. Sport with his deep love of the chase, could not resist and in spite of our efforts to train him not to chase automobiles, we found him one morning dead beside the dusty road. He was given a formal burial down by the barn and his grave appropriately marked with a cross.

Cats are nice animals, you pat them on the head or stroke their fur and they purr. If they are not fed, they do not politely stand on their hind legs and beg or bark or wag their tails, cats simply "meow". But in spite of this limited vocabulary, our next pet was a cat, a Maltese with three white feet. After the demise of Sport, much love and affection was showered on Boots.

Now Boots was not one of those cats who liked to lie around the house and wait for his milk. He was off in the fields looking for game, and often would bring home a gopher or field mouse, and I am sorry to say, sometimes a young quail or other small bird.

His desire to roam and hunt brought disaster to Boots.

Across the road was a wonderful stand of alfalfa. Boots spent hours in this field looking for game. The alfalfa was ready to make into hay so one day Mr. Walker, the owner, hitched his team to a mowing machine and cut the alfalfa. Just why Boots was not frightened enough to run away from the hideous noise we never did understand.

We had just come in for supper when we heard his piteous cries. Six inches of his tail and the lower joints of both his beautiful hind legs were gone. He had dragged himself home through the dust by his front feet. We bathed and bound his wounds and Boots lived with us for a time with his stubs. The children all showered love and affection on him, but he was never the same. Gone was his roving wild spirit and desire to hunt, although once or twice he still tried to get out and hunt for gophers. Apparently he could not stand a life of ease and luxury and about a year later he sickened, and in spite of all our efforts, he too died and joined our animal cemetery down near the barn.

Henry was a water spaniel with shiny silk red hair. He was dignified and loyal. How Henry loved the water. When we swam he was always with us and whenever and wherever there was water Henry was there. He enjoyed chasing the squirrels and gophers that were flooded out of their holes when we irrigated our pasture land.

At our command he dug deep holes always pretending that he was in search of some animal.

Henry was soon taught not to chase automobiles although you could see that he wanted to badly. He would look around at you hoping for a command to pursue. He never cheated by chasing cars when he knew you were not watching. For a dog he seemed to possess a great integrity.

When we moved to town Henry went with us. He adapted to city life, but was happiest when we took him for a swim. A fishing trip was spoiled by his love for water, so we finally had to leave him at home except when we were swimming only.

One morning Henry did not appear for breakfast. We called and called. We thought he might be sick or hurt. Finally we found his still form out in back of the barn with a bullet hole through his beautiful head. Apparently he was guarding our place from some one who was trying to steal our horse, and the thief had shot him because he was being attacked.

Our next dog we did not choose. Snyder chose us. How we ever got the name of Snyder no one has ever been able to determine.

We were having a wonderful time one day with friends in our front yard when a miserable looking little cur came in the front gate. He was about the color of a wild coyote and about half as tall, tan with fine black stripes down his brown and gray back. His tail was between his legs. He had no doubt been the object of abuse. To us boys, he was just a tramp dog. We sought clods from the flower beds and began to throw them at the dog.

But not so Little Sis. She cried out, "Stop," and ran

to Snyder and threw her arms around his neck and held him to her. "He is my dog."

And her dog he was for many years. He was also the pet of the family and became the pet of Tulare.

As I recalled the aristocratic carriage of Henry and many other fine dogs of my friends and neighbors, I held some resentment toward this Snyder, who had assumed his way into our house. One morning as I hurried to school, I cut across a vacant lot and observed that Snyder was following me. Not wishing for him to be with me at school, I reached down to pick up a clod to drive him back, but lo, in the clod was a silver coin. I kept the coin and simply tossed the clod in Snyder's direction with a command to go home, which he did.

About two weeks later, I again observed Snyder slipping along in back of me, and again I reached down for a clod, and the second time discovered a silver coin in the clod. This time I did not throw the clod as I asked myself, "Do you suppose this dog is good luck and brings me silver coins?"

Thereafter I entered into a verbal agreement with Snyder that he was not to follow me unless invited, and if he did come to school he would hide out until school was over and then return home with me. I am happy to report that Snyder followed this agreement to the letter with one exception.

Snyder was a social animal and loved all people, with a few exceptions. He ate most any food that human beings would eat except cucumbers, I think he was influenced about the cucumbers by Papa who said, "They are poison." I think they gave him a stomach ache.

When I came home from school one of my favorite

snacks was one overall pocket full of almonds in the shell and another pocket full of sweet muscat raisins on the stem. If Snyder saw me cracking almonds he would stand up on his hind legs and beg until I gave him his share. He cracked the nuts with aplomb and then begged for raisins. Many dogs wolfed down food, but Snyder would spit out the seeds from the muscat raisins with a royal flourish.

He enjoyed his vegetables raw as well as cooked, and would eat lettuce from the garden or dig up a carrot to indulge his appetite. No doubt, he knew all about the vitamin C it contained.

There were two kinds of people Snyder hated, and one was the butcher boy.

In Tulare there were no super markets, and if you wished meat, you went to the meat market and picked it out or you phoned the market and told them what you wished and it was delivered to you. Most of our meat was delivered by the butcher boy. Snyder hated him and would ferociously snap at his ankles. This butcher boy quit, but Snyder hated the new boy with the same fury. This went on and on. Mama tried her best to bring about a reconcilation between the butcher boy and Snyder.

"No," said the butcher boy, "I have never tried to strike Snyder, in fact I have tried to be friendly."

One day Mama decided to resolve this problem so she explained to Snyder, "The butcher boy is our good friend and brings us fresh meat." She untied the package of meat, cut off some for Snyder and asked the butcher boy to feed him.

So the boy fed Snyder and Snyder seemed to relish the tidbits although he kept an eye on the boy all the time he was eating. The boy patted Snyder on the head and it appeared a truce was declared. But as the butcher boy started around the side of the house toward the gate, Snyder tore after him in full pursuit and this time he was not content to nip at his heels, but leaped for the seat of his pants. That was the last time this boy would come to our back door if Snyder were in the yard.

Snyder had the same attitude toward the next butcher boy and towards his successor. If he had been a vegetarian, I could have understood his attitude, but these were the men who brought him his cherished meat. He hated them and how he let them know he hated them!

One day when Little Sis, still small, was playing out in front of the house Snyder started barking furiously. It sounded as though he were about to attack a prowler. We hurried around the house, and there was a dirty old tramp right near Little Sis. Snyder was her constant companion. Either the tramp made some motion towards her or else Snyder thought he did, and was ready to defend his mistress with his life if necessary.

One day we were in the house playing Indian and Little Sis was the papoose. We had her all wrapped up and bound to a board just like a real papoose. She could not get out anyway. She was left leaning up against the fireplace and I guess there was some fire in the fireplace. Some friends called from outside and we went outside to visit, leaving Little Sis leaning up by the fireplace. Snyder didn't like this. He began barking and running around until we finally came in to see what was the trouble. As soon as we had released Little Sis, he was happy again.

One hot summer afternoon a lady came to call on Mama and sat in a rocking chair fanning herself with a big cardboard fan. She was large and vigorous, and as she rocked the chair moved slowly across the floor. Snyder loved to come into the house where it was cool downstairs on summer days and sleep on the cold floor. He was snoring gently near where this friend was rocking. Suddenly the chair rocker came down on his tail and he tore out of the house with a terrific yowl. Sympathetic Little Sis followed him out. She would fix up her little friend. She remembered that mother had used turpentine as antiseptic for cuts. This should do very well for Snyder and so she made generous application on Snyder's sore tail. No doubt she was a little careless in the application, for Snyder tore around the house and up and down the street for fully half an hour yelling and howling before we could catch him and bathe him and sooth his injured feelings.

Little Sis sobbed, "I didn't mean to hurt Snyder. Truly, I didn't, Mama."

So Mama explained to her, "You don't ever put turpentine on any animal, for where there is fur it will always burn. Also you probably spilled some of the turpentine on some of the tender parts of Snyder's body."

Snyder learned to climb ladders, walk on his hind legs, and a score of other tricks Little Sis taught him.

Often we found him dressed in baby clothes with a hood tied over his head. Little Sis wheeled him about in an old baby buggy for hours, but he patiently allowed her to "doll him up" as she would say. He objected to diapers but everything else he permitted with patience.

A strange cat crossed the path one day as Snyder, Little Sis and carriage were out for a stroll. Snyder, forgetting his costume, jumped from the carriage and gave chase. He tripped on the garments and rolled head over heels. Quickly regaining his feet he tried it again with no better luck. After the third attempt Snyder, chagrined, gave up the chase, for the cat was a block away.

Little Sis spanked him gently, "Look, Snyder, when you are dressed up you are my baby and you must not chase cats."

Snyder looked up at her crestfallen. He never chased cats again when he was dressed up.

Snyder started to school with Little Sis and seemed to pass successfully from grade to grade. As he got older he escorted her to school and then returned home, returning to the school at the time school was dismissed in order to escort her home again. He was greatly disturbed if she stayed after school to practice for some program and greeted her with extra warmth upon her appearance. I used to think that he was almost too affectionate with his face licking and jumping up and down so much, but that was Snyder and he had special privileges.

Snyder was not only interested in acquiring a general education, but he seemed to be especially anxious to improve the spiritual side of his life for he never missed a Sunday at Sunday school and church, that is if he could help it. The only way to prevent his attendance was to lock him in the house. Many times we locked him in the back yard, but he managed to get out somehow. Our first knowledge of his presence was his gentle snoring under the pew. On those warm days the church door was left open and if it were not Snyder would slip in with some late comer.

Friends accepted Snyder as one of the family and if they thought the dog was peculiar, they probably thought the family was odd to have such a dog. Almost everybody in town knew Snyder and he was a friend to everyone. They accepted his eccentricities just as we did.

One Sunday morning Snyder was careless about his position in church, and left his tail out from under the pew. A stout lady arrived at church late and stepped directly upon Snyder's outstretched tail. Service was interrupted for a few moments, and Snyder was locked in the house for a few Sundays.

It was not always possible to lock Snyder in the house on Sunday mornings. He seemed to have an uncanny knowledge that this was the Sabbath day. During the school year, we could understand why he would know that it was Sunday because it came after Saturday when all of the kids were home. But even in the summer time, Snyder knew when Sunday came around, and generally he would hide for hours appearing at church later and in time for the sermon through which he slept and snored.

Snyder lived with us for many years for he lived to be an old dog. One night he passed away in his sleep.

When you have had a dog like Snyder in your home, you simply cannot live without a dog. The next dog was a white, curly haired female, which Mama called Fluffo. I don't know the breed and I don't know why she was named Fluffo, but she was in every way the antithesis of Snyder.

First, she was a lady and a queen. She looked royal and she expected to be treated royally. She was not allowed to roam and her education was not in the public schools, nor was she permitted to attend church services. It may be that most of us children were away at school and did not corrupt this new addition to the family. She was strictly Mama's dog, and Mama's pet, and Mama's companion. She, too, lived for many happy years in our old home and brought companionship to Mama and to her friends with her tricks and with her charming reaction to people.

Horses are a lot of fun too. I remember the first fancy two-seated carriage with its fringe top and side curtains that Papa bought one spring. There was a new whip in the whip socket and how we did all sparkle riding to church in this snappy outfit as we rambled down the dusty roads. There were times when the road department spread old straw to keep down the dust, but generally we left behind us a stream of dust which curled up and drifted into the buggy. That sort of dusty soil was wonderful to walk through barefooted. Papa and Mama hated it most when we were dressed up and going to church or to some other fancy doings.

When we first moved out to the Fry ranch we had one horse which we got from one of our friends. Her name was Nellie. She was our riding horse or we hitched her to a run-about from which the back seat could be removed if you wished to haul a load.

During the summer months, sometimes Jesse and I would drive Papa out to the ranch where he worked in the office. We would drive back home to do some of our regular chores, or ride to town, or perhaps just play around. Jesse loved to drive and being older he was always in the driver's seat.

Every buggy was equipped with a whip which was placed in the socket in the right hand corner of the carriage in front of the seat. But Jesse never liked this kind of whip and he would always take it out and leave it home. He preferred to rig up his own whip from a strap which he had wrapped around his wrist. This worked just fine and he did not injure Nellie or any other horse with this strap for he tapped them gently. The horse, however, was always surprised to be hit with a strap rather than with the properly designed whip.

One day when we were coming home from the ranch, Jesse hit Nellie with the strap. Startled, she jumped forward jerking the buggy. Jesse was all set to hit her the second time with the strap and was swinging it in the air, but he was thrown off balance and the end of the strap went through the buggy spokes and around the rim of the wheel. Jesse was jerked forward between the shafts and the wheel and onto the ground. He took the reins with him. Fortunately, the strap around his wrist broke and he was not dragged through the soft dust into which he had fallen.

But here I was in a buggy with Nellie galloping down the road and no reins. I looked about for some means of stopping the horse. I could see nothing except her tail, so I reached forward and grabbed her tail in both hands as I shouted, 'Whoa, Nellie! Whoa, Nellie!"

I was glad Nellie was an understanding horse and came to a gradual halt.

Nellie took Big Sis, Jesse and me to school in a buggy which we unhitched at school and hitched up again after school to drive home. There was a short cut to school that saved nearly half a mile and which we generally took even though it went through an old dry creek bed.

One time when we were returning from school, we found this old creek bed full of water. We pulled up and looked over the flood which had come from the sudden melting of snow in the mountains. A fill for a new road down stream had effectively dammed the water. We finally decided to go through, otherwise, we would have to go back around town and drive an extra mile. Everything went fine until we got out in the middle of the flood and the water started coming up into the bed of the buggy. Jesse tried to get his feet up on the seat and dropped the lines into the water.

Nellie stopped. Here we were in the middle of the wide creek, water in all directions, no reins and Nellie refused to budge.

Big Sis said, "Oh, what will we do now? We'll have to swim out."

None of us could swim well and we had on our good school clothes. Jesse could swim hardly at all because of his bad leg. But with his general determination, he finally decided to climb out on the shafts which were just barely out of water and reach the lines. This he did and soon we were on our way home to tell Mama of our adventure in the water.

Mama said, "Jesse was very brave to climb out over the shafts to get the reins. But next time don't try to drive through deep water."

We all loved Nellie. We rode horseback on her when

she was not hitched to a buggy. We always treated her with kindness and respect and she responded.

If Big Sis were unable to go to school because of illness or something else, Jesse and I would ride double horseback to school, and we rode her frequently just for the fun about the ranch or about the dusty roads. Nellie was never sick. She was ready always to take us places. She was our friend. One day when Jesse was riding her home from school she fell over dead. There was great sorrow in our home that night for we had lost a wonderful friend.

While we were living on the Fry ranch there were other horses in our lives. Some were in the big pasture next to our ranch and we were responsible for letting people board their horses in this pasture. We also used some of the horses for plowing or ranch work, and sometimes we caught them and rode them. The owners had free board for their horses if we were allowed to use them. All horses were turned out in the pasture when they were not being used, and when we needed one we all got out and chased him into the corral so that we could put a bridle on him.

One day I got too close to a sorrel and was kicked in the stomach. I keeled over and Papa and Jesse ran up to see if I were dead. As soon as I got my breath back I went on to help them catch the horse. I guess I never learned how close one should get to a horse for two or three months later, I was grazed in the head by a hoof and my temple cut. I learned then to be a little more cautious about horses' feet.

Our favorite horse was a buckskin mare named Dolly. She smartly pulled our fringed surrey about town, for we moved back into Tulare shortly after we acquired her. She was kind and gentle with all the children. Three of us could ride her at one time, but if the fourth tried to get on her back, she would start bucking until we were all off. Dolly was quite a traveler and could go many miles in a day without any special care.

Jesse used to ride her to deliver papers when it was too rainy to ride his bike, and she knew the route as well as he, for on two or three occasions when he was sick I took his route and discovered that she knew just where the papers were to be delivered. She was a smart horse.

Dolly did not know that someone had put up a swing on a tree limb and one dark evening she took Jesse under this limb and he was jerked off into the mud. She got excited that time and came home. Then the whole family was upset. Poor Jesse had to walk nearly a mile in the rain before he got home and all the time Mama and Papa were worried about him and wondered if he were dead some place. He finally came in limping and he was pretty mad. He wanted to lick Dolly for taking him under a limb, but Papa and Mama restrained him and explained that a horse would not have enough sense to know that a swing had been put up over the week end. I had to go out and finish the paper route in the rain. I remember, I got pretty wet and got sick and missed some school all because of the swing being put up in the wrong place.

First thing we knew, Dolly was going to have a baby colt. Papa thought she should not be driven so much and we kept her in the barn or else in a corral we had across the alley from the barn. One day we went out and there was a beautiful buckskin colt just the same color as his mother.

Dick, for that was his name, grew rapidly, and in a couple of years we had him broken to the harness, although we did not use him to pull the buggy or ride much until he was three. Papa thought he ought to be full grown before he was treated as a horse.

At last Dick was a well developed young horse, fully a foot taller than his mother. Papa didn't think we ought to keep two horses in town, and told us we would have to decide which horse we were going to keep. This was a serious question and we debated it for as long as we could put it off, and we finally decided to sell Dolly and keep Dick. Somewhat later we discovered that we had been short-changed by this transaction, for Dick would ride only two of us at one time. If a third person tried to ride, he would start bucking. He could buck harder than Dolly.

Squirrels, ducks, canaries, gold fish, raccoons and numerous cats were pets that commanded deepest affection. For a while we even had a gopher, but he bit Jesse severely and Papa insisted that we get rid of him.

Everybody on a farm owned a cow or two, and so did we. Papa never liked to milk and so somehow or other at quite an early age, I was taught to milk. It seemed to me that Jesse was protected a little too much for some things he could not do because he could not get around fast enough. It seemed to me that he could have learned to sit still and milk a cow.

Papa and Mama didn't think so. They said, "Jesse is too nervous and we are afraid that he will make the cow nervous and she won't give so much milk."

So they taught me to milk. Mama did not like to milk either, and Big Sis would not milk so I became the milker.

I guess the experience was good because I got a job later on the basis of it, and it helped when I ran a dairy myself for awhile when I was in high school. It may have been that I was really fond of cows. I found that they were quiet and generally good natured and didn't talk back.

There were certain things about cows that you had to observe. One did not let them out to have too much fresh green feed. If you did they might get bloated. This appeared to be a form of indigestion common among people who have ulcers, which is really just a lot of gas on the stomach. One way you relieved a cow was to stick a knife in it along the flank right in front of the hind leg. When I used to hear people talk about having indigestion I wondered why they did not use the same method, it brought such quick relief.

When we moved to town, we took old bossy with us. She was a red brindle cow with white spots, and every year she gave us a nice little red calf that we enjoyed petting and spoiling until it was old enough to wean, and then Papa gave it away. When we protested he said, "We can't run a farm even if we do have a quarter of a city block in back of our house for pasture."

I was quite an expert milker. Our kitten, Puss, used to follow me out to milk the cow in the late afternoons. She never appeared when I milked the cow in the morning. I suppose it was too early for her to arise. She would always come out in the evening. She would smell the warm, fresh milk and cry for some. I practised squirting some of the warm milk into her face. She loved this procedure. And as time went on, I became quite proficient in hitting her face and mouth. All that went on her face she licked off anyway and got the full benefit of it.

Snyder discovered that this was a way to get good

fresh milk, and he would come out and chase Puss away and beg for milk. So I learned to take care of his great hunger in the same manner. This method of feeding the animals went along very nicely, but one day Little Sis came out and saw how expertly I could feed the cat and dog, so she asked if she couldn't have some milk that way. I declined, I said "No, it'll make trouble."

"I'm just as good as the cat and dog," she stamped her foot.

"Well, certainly," I replied.

"Then give me some milk too," she said.

I instructed her to turn her head sideways so that no milk would get on her hair and expertly brought the stream around to her mouth. She claimed this was delicious and she, too, started coming out every evening if she were free from other duties, to have some warm fresh milk. This went along for several days until one night just as I was in the process of bringing the stream around to her little mouth, Mama called from the back gate. "Little Sis, what are you doing?"

Little Sis turned her head just as Mama called and got the full effect of milk all through her ear and over her hair and down on her dress. That was the last time she had fresh milk by the short cut method I had devised.

Cows are such kind, quiet friends. They don't talk much. They just listen. Sometimes as I went out to milk, I might be concerned about some problem at school or elsewhere, and I would find old bossy lying down chewing her cud, and so I would just sit down on her back and contemplate some of my problems. If there was something that had to be talked out, I would tell her about it, and she would sagely chew her cud and listen, sometimes responding but always only with a very soft sound. Mama says that on two or three occasions, I did not return from milking for an hour, she would go to see where I was and find me sitting on the cow contemplating life and its problems.

Chapter XI

MY BIG BROTHER JESSE

The last year we lived in Texas, my brother Jesse hurt his hip while wrestling with some friends. For weeks he lay in agony in his bed. We could hear his cry of pain during the daytime and his groans at night. None of the children was permitted to go into his bedroom. After many weeks, I was allowed to peek into his room for just a minute.

Jesse was six or seven years of age and Mama had long before cut off his beautiful, silky blond curls, but as I looked into his bedroom, his golden hair shone as a crown upon his head. His big brown eyes were sunk deep into his head and surrounded by black circles. His face was pale and drawn. Straps held him firmly in his bed on his back, all except his right leg raised in the air and fastened with weights to a rack at the foot of the bed.

He smiled cheerfully when he saw me and said, "I'll be out of here in a couple of weeks and we will have fun together again." I could only smile for the sight sickened me.

Mama explained to me that his hip joint was injured and it was necessary to have the weights on his leg to keep the socket apart so that it could heal. It was necessary, also, to drain pus from the joint. She explained that the doctors said Jesse had tuberculosis of the hip joint. Doctors did not know as much then as they do now.

Months later Jesse was up and around on two crutches. He could not put much weight on his right foot for a long time and then only to touch his toe. He continued to be quite frail for over a year and on the doctor's recommendation the family decided to move to California for his health.

The magic of x-ray had not been discovered. The doctors did all they could for Jesse. He was just not privileged to live in the era of x-ray and wonder drugs, but from frail, puny childhood, through Mama's tender care, he grew into dynamic manhood and then in the prime of his life he was gone.

My brother Jesse first saw the light of dawn in Lebanon, Oregon. Immediately upon his birth, he cried out for food and for the forty years which he lived, he continued to have that hearty appetite except for those few years of his affliction.

While we lived in Downey, Jesse continued to get around on two crutches, cheerful always and determined to do physical things that every other youngster did. Grandpa encouraged him and Mama was there always tenderly preparing special food for him and watching over his welfare lest he reinjure his hip joint.

After we moved to Tulare, he was able to discard one of his crutches for now he could put his foot down and partly use it for walking. It was quite apparent by this time that one leg would be shorter.

Jesse was always sensitive about his lameness. Once when he was small and was trying to play with other children, a boy remarked, "You can't play with us. You're just an old cripple."

Jesse came to Mama with tears streaming down his cheeks, "The boys say I can't play with them 'cause I'm a cripple."

Mama comforted him, "Son, you're just crippled in your leg, but a person who says mean things about your lameness is crippled in his heart."

While he was still on crutches in Tulare, Mama began to give him a daily tablespoon full of emulsion of cod-liver oil. He did not care for this tonic, but the doctor recommended it to improve his appetite. In order to induce him to think that it tasted good, I used to beg to be allowed to have some also. The tonic was rather expensive and generally all I got was a chance to lick the spoon after he had his dose of the medicine, which he thought was vile.

Either the cod-liver oil or the California sunshine restored his appetite for he was such a hearty eater thereafter that Mama used to say to him, "Jesse, I'm afraid that we overdid the cod-liver oil. What do you think about it?"

Jesse generally replied craftily, "Mama, you cook such good food that I just can't help eating so much."

With the return of his appetite, Jesse grew into a robust boy. He wanted to discard his one crutch and so Papa arranged to have his foot measured for an extension so that he could walk without limping. The first extension made of steel, was very light and wore out rapidly on the sandy soil. The next shoe was built up two inches below the sole with a second sole. Later on this shoe was improved so that he really walked on tiptoe on that foot with his weight resting on the heel of his shoe. This he felt made him quite inconspicious as his long trouser leg covered most of the shoe.

Jesse was determined to do anything that any other boy could do. He participated in a limited way in many outdoor games. He was a good rider and spent lots of time in the saddle. He did not care much for fishing or hunting and never became an excellent swimmer.

Mama encouraged Jesse in every way. Papa would sometimes caution, "Well, Son, don't overdo it, remember that you are lame." But Mama would always reply, "I think Jesse can do anything that anyone else can do."

He loved horses and drove a team whenever he could get his hands on the reins. On the farm, he learned to follow a team down the furrow all day. As he grew older he worked on hay balers and became a proficient finish carpenter. These exercises helped him to develop a deep chest and broad powerful shoulders. He was not as tall as Grandpa Jonathan but possessed the same powerful physique and the hearty, friendly laughter of our grandfather.

When we moved back into town, Jesse located a paper route and daily delivered papers on a bicycle. Later, he worked in the newspaper office and learned to operate a linotype.

In high school he turned out for the basketball team but never could quite make the first squad. As manager he arranged many of our games and our transportation. In tennis he really excelled and was one of the two best players in our high school. This was indeed remarkable with one leg two inches shorter than the other.

Our family decided that we ought to have a tennis court nearer home so we built a clay court on some lots near our home. Jesse and I and our friends laid out this court, conditioned the grounds, put up back stops at each end, and even built a tropical pavilion of bamboo poles and palm tree leaves.

This tennis court became a social center for our neighborhood and for many of our friends from other sections of town. Many a hot summer, we would get up at five o'clock in the morning and play in order to keep in good form.

Often when friends came early in the morning, Mama would come out and invite them to have breakfast with us when the game was finished. Ham and eggs with hot biscuits and honey and fruit. Hot biscuits were her specialty and everyone called Mama, "The Biscuit Queen."

One day, Jesse said of our tennis court, "Well, all the work we did building that court and keeping it in condition has paid off. Our Big Sis has captured a boy friend and they are going to be married."

We all liked Ralph very much and were glad to have this preliminary announcement. They really were married about a year later.

Jesse was popular with men and women and he always had a number of girl friends. Some nights he would stay out later than our parents approved. I recall one night that he was not home by 2 a.m. so Papa got out of bed, dressed, and walked a couple of blocks to Jesse's girl friend's house. There they were, three couples on the front porch talking away and having a good time, but Papa brought Jesse home. Jesse never stayed out that late again while he was in high school.

Jesse worked his way through Pomona College with some assistance from Papa and Mama. He waited tables, washed dishes and did janitor work, but most of all he liked his work with the local newspaper. He was editor of the college paper one year, took part in the debating teams and, in spite of all this outside activity, he received excellent grades.

Before Jesse graduated from Pomona College, he decided to be a teacher so we all helped him to go to the University of California where he spent the next year and won both his high school teaching credentials and his master's degree. The authorities at the university told him that it could not be done in one year, that was before he did it. After he succeeded in securing both, they told him that it had never been done before.

Jesse never could have survived his childhood affliction without the tender nursing and loving care which Mama constantly gave him. Even after he was hopping around on crutches, Mama used to say to us, "Please remember that your brother is crippled. Treat him with tenderness and kindness and if necessary, let him impose on you a little for that will not hurt you any and it will help him a great deal."

As Jesse gained his strength and threw away his crutches, he asked no quarter from anyone. In physical games and in indoor games of skill and chance, he excelled for he was aggressive, brilliant and filled with a desire to win.

During World War I after I had enlisted in the service, he, too, wanted to join, but because of his short leg he was not accepted. He talked to me about it only once, but he tried the Army, the Navy and the Coast Guard, and all turned him down.

The YWCA was the principal recreational guardian of troops during World War I for there was no USO. At the University of California he learned that he would be eligible for work with the YMCA as an educational director so he traveled to Tulare to talk the matter over with Papa and Mama. Both of them were still a little inclined to shelter Jesse and expressed some objection. I think they were worried for fear I would be overseas in the war zone. At any rate, they tried to discourage him. I cannot report all of the conversation which took place between them, but Little Sis told me many years later some of the words she overheard when she came suddenly into the house.

"Son, you are a grown man and you have a right to decide for yourself. I have already stated that I do not believe that this is the best thing for you," Mama was overheard to say.

"Mama, all my life I have done what you wanted me to do. I have respected your wishes at all times and you have been a wonderful mother. You have been such a good parent that you have often made me forget that I am just a damned cripple. I've tried to get into the Army, the Navy and the Coast Guard and they have all refused me because I'm a cripple. Now I believe I have this opportunity to get into the YMCA as an educational director and serve my country just as my brother is doing."

"Very well, son, and may God's blessing go with you," replied Mama.

Jesse joined the YMCA staff and became educational director for the Army at the Presidio in San Francisco and assistant director for the western division. After World War I, I was discharged at New York, but my first port of call was the Presidio at San Francisco. I welcomed my brother in his YMCA uniform. I was proud of his rank and title, and I was proud that he had served his country in his own way for he was still a hero to me as he had always been, for he was my big brother Jesse.

Jesse taught in Marysville High School for one year and the following year was invited to teach in Tulare High School and some time later became vice principal.

I did not live in Tulare when he taught there, but Little Sis was in his class one year. She said he was the hardest teacher she ever had. When he discovered that she was to be in his class, he called her aside and said, "Look, kid, it's bad to have you in my class, but one thing you may be sure of, no one will ever be able to say that I showed you any favoritism because you are my sister. You had better have your lessons every day because I expect a perfect answer from you about some question every day." Little Sis said she never let him down.

I was principal of the Tulare High School many years later and numerous residents of that community said to me, "Your brother Jesse was the toughest teacher I ever had, but I learned more from him than any teacher. The things he taught us, we have always remembered."

Another said, "Your brother Jesse was a shrewd teacher and a fair one. When it came time for a final examination he would say, "Now I am going to give you a list of a hundred questions for you to study for the final, I will use ten questions from this list, is that fair enough?' We all agreed that it was fair enough and soon discovered that the hundred questions covered everything that we were supposed to have studied during the course. Students who studied got good grades."

From Tulare, Jesse was invited to go to Delano and be principal and superintendent of the high school there. While he was there, he fell in love and married Vera Beall, a home making teacher in the high school. The boys and girls in his school idealized him and he, in turn, kept student life at Delano High School challenging and full of activity.

Chapter XII

SWIMMING, FISHING, HUNTING AND

RECREATION

Swimming was our favorite sport in warm late spring and hot summer when water flowed in all of the irrigating canals. Many ranchers south and west of town had reservoirs supplied by artesian wells. In late summer when the irrigation canals were dry, we would drive south of town to the bayou which provided both good swimming and good fishing, or we would drive west four miles to one of the most popular reservoirs. Here, for a small fee, you could swim all day and picnic on the grassy areas. How we did eat! After swimming it seemed there was never enough food, but our family loved swimming and enjoyed many happy times at this favorite swimming place.

Most of the time we walked to our swims in canals, two or three miles on a hot dusty road for a chance to swim and cool off, and then back again we would trudge to our homes along the same dusty road. Occasionally we would catch a ride with some farmer going to town in his buggy or wagon.

Next to swimming, fishing was our favorite sport. The irrigation canals brought fish down from the rivers and at times we could even catch them by hand. Sometimes they washed out upon our land, which we were irrigating, and we could catch them with the aid of a shovel.

We enjoyed irrigating for we would flood our fields between the small levees which surrounded each square and allow the water to soak into the ground. This brought out ground squirrels and gophers, and other varmints, and we would have fun catching them with the aid of our dogs. Some we kept for pets but most of them were hurt so badly by the dogs that they had to be killed.

Fishing was a year around sport for there were no rules and regulations that required license, or limiting seasons. Most of our fish we caught with worms. There were trout, perch, sunfish, carp, bass, but best of all were the catfish. Their thorny fins sometimes made it difficult to disengage the hook, but their meat was white, juicy and tender, and we loved to cook them on the bank of the stream where they were landed. Generally, we cleaned them, put salt and butter inside, wrapped them in oiled paper and butcher paper, covered them with mud and cooked them in the coals of a fire. Fish never tasted so good.

Hunting was our next favorite sport. I did not own a gun but sometimes was permitted to go with older boys as they hunted for squirrels, cottontails or rabbits.

My first gun I made with a piece of pipe. The pipe was small, just large enough to hold a small fire-cracker. I used this as a noise maker and sometimes we would shoot rocks or home-made darts with this gun. Even small boys were allowed to buy black powder in the store, and so we began to shoot black powder in our home-made guns. The father of one of my friends was a plumber and was able to get scrap pipe for us to use.

We made some good Fourth of July cannons from pipe, but they made so much noise that some of the neighbors complained, So Mama thought that we had better quit making and shooting cannons.

One July Fourth we planned to wake everyone in our community with a big salute from our cannon, which we were going to follow with giant firecrackers. Bunny wanted to get up early too to join the fun, so we tied a string to her big toe and hung it out of the front second story window. Unfortunately it hung right where Big Sis and Ralph passed when they came home late from the show. They did not know what the string was, so they pulled it and awakened Bunny. Sis made her take off the string so she did not get down next morning in time to see us shoot the cannon.

We continued to have fire-cracker guns and between the Fourth of July and Chinese New Year, which came along about the last of January, we had ammunition for our fire-cracker guns.

One gun, made of a piece of pipe glued to a stock just like a regular rifle, had a removable wooden plug to close the back end. A hole drilled in the top provided an opening through which the fire-cracker fuse was placed for lighting.

Jesse wanted to shoot this gun one day and I gave it to him to shoot. He lit the fire-cracker and held it up in front of his face pretending to shoot at something. The wooden plug in the back of the gun was not in tight and it blew out hitting him below the eye. He was not injured seriously but Mama forbade me to use the fire-cracker gun any more. As a result, I begged for an air-gun and bought a second-hand gun from one of my friends for one dollar.

Neither Mama nor I knew that all the boys in our neighborhood who had BB guns were shooting at each other. Just a day or two after I bought my gun, I was out in the back yard cutting some kindling wood for the stove and fireplace when I heard a thump near me. I went on working and pretty soon there was another thump and then a third thump which hit me on the leg. I hid behind an outbuilding and soon I heard some of the boys laughing.

"You had better get your gun," one said, "so that you can shoot back."

I got my gun and we shot back and forth. No one was injured in the fracas, but about two weeks later one of my friends got a BB shot in his cheek and all the parents in the neighborhood got together and stopped the BB gun shooting.

While we were carrying on this guerrilla warfare some of the boys built tree-houses so they could shoot down on their friends. That started a craze and nearly every boy built a tree-house. After our guns were taken away, we decided to build a cave where we could hide things. We dug a cave back under the ground for a distance of forty feet. It was well below the surface. We worked for days getting the dirt out of this cave, but one week end after a heavy rain, part of it fell in and we were forbidden to have caves any more.

Next year the bicycle craze hit town and nearly every boy in town had a bicycle. It was fun to ride up and down the street, but it was more fun to ride to swimming or fishing. This made it easier to get to our favorite swimming holes.

One of our very best friends had a big irrigation canal running through his farm. A big head-gate controlled the water flowing into smaller canals, and in front of this head-gate was a wonderful place for swimming. We built a boat out of 1x12's and with a little bailing it was quite seaworthy.

Jesse was a little fearful of deep water and one day he was riding in the boat with two or three other boys when one of the boys started rocking the boat. Jesse told him to desist—that he did not like deep water. But the boy kept on rocking the boat, so Jesse hit him over the head with an oar and knocked him into the water. He stopped rocking the boat after that, but Jesse was not allowed to visit this place for some time.

Another time, Jesse and a friend visiting from San Francisco rode their bikes out to the same ranch for a swim and a boat ride. On the way back to town his friend, Harry, in the dusk of the evening, saw a black cat with a white stripe down its back running along the road. Harry speeded up his bicycle to chase the cat and as it turned into the bushes he jumped off of his bike trying to land on the cat. Well, it was not the kind of kitty that Harry thought it was, and he went on home smelling awful.

Jesse thought he did not get mixed up with the skunk. When he came home, we were already sitting down for dinner for he was late. Jesse came in the door laughing, "You ought to've seen what Harry got mixed up with on the way home."

Mama held her nose, "We don't need to see what Harry got mixed up with, we can smell what you got mixed up with."

Jesse protested that he was not anywhere near the skunk, but Mama took him aside and made him bury his clothes in the ground for a few days to get the smell off. After a good bath he was allowed to associate with the rest of us, but he still stank.

After I couldn't use my BB gun, I was permitted to sell it to a friend who lived a long way from us. I begged Papa and Mama for a .22 rifle and they said if I earned the money myself I could buy a Hamilton rifle. The Hamilton was an odd sort of rifle with a very short barrel. You inserted the cartridge about half way down the barrel. The barrel was steel with a brass lining.

I finally earned enough money to buy the rifle and Papa accompanied me when I first went hunting with it. Actually, most of the time we spent just shooting at tin cans sitting on a fence post. Papa was a good shot, much better than I.

While I was waiting to get my Hamilton, I was inventing a new device to get me into trouble. Most of our bicycles had carbide lamps on the front. You put the carbide in a container in the bottom of the lamp below another little tank which held water. You opened up a little valve and as the water trinkled into the carbide, it created a gas which lighted your bicycle if you were traveling at night. The gas was also highly explosive as I learned.

One Sunday afternoon I was experimenting around the back yard. No friends over, and there did not seem to be any place to go. I found a can which had a small opening near the bottom with a metal tube protruding from the side. I decided to see if I could not make a bigger generator for carbide gas. So I put some carbide in a little tin can with some water on it and put the bigger can upside down over it with the tube at the top. I waited until I could hear the gas coming out the top and then I lighted a match to it. It made a beautiful flame.

After the little bit of water was used up, I took the big can off and put more water on the carbide This time I neglected to wait for the gas to fill the big container. As I struck a match to the opening there was a terrific explosion and the big can sailed into the air about sixty feet. Little Sis was near me watching the performance. Fortunately the can did not come down on either of us.

All of our neighbors were alerted by the noise and Mama came out to see what was going on. When she discovered that I was playing with a real explosive she suggested that maybe I had been endangering the life of my little sister and that perhaps I had best spend the afternoon in bed so that I would not get into any more trouble.

Finally, I got my fill of blowing up things. The father of one of my friends moved to a new farm subdivision four or five miles east of town. Most of his forty acres were covered with huge valley oak trees. The land was exceedingly rich, but the trees had to be removed before the land could be farmed. So crews were brought in to cut down the trees. The trunks of the trees were so big through that it was difficult to saw them so they decided to split the fallen tree trunks by blasting. So I visited my friend every Saturday.

We would use a huge auger which was about two inches in diameter and drill a hole down into the center of the fallen tree trunk. Into this we would place a couple of pounds of black blasting powder, push a fuse down into it, tamp the hole full of moist earth, light the fuse and run. A terrific explosion blew the huge log apart. Actually, it was hard work drilling a two inch hole into a log nearly four feet thick although we went only half way. After a few week ends of this blasting, I decided that I had enough explosions. I had my .22 Hamilton now so I did not blast any more stumps.

Papa and Mama were afraid all the time that we would blow ourselves up while we were blowing up the stumps. They did not like to have me take this trip out into the country either for my friend had just acquired a new motorcycle and I was riding on the back of it. The road was rough for the last mile and one-half and I was thrown from the motorcycle several times. Fortunately, I only skinned my knee.

I used my Hamilton rifle for about a year, but it began to get too easy on the trigger. Just the slightest touch of the trigger and it would be discharged. One time it went off while I was carrying it. The bullet just grazed the edge of my right shoe. So I traded it off to another boy for a second hand Stevens rifle which I used for many years.

Papa taught me how to use a rifle and taught me that it was important to be extremely careful. "A .22 bullet," he said, "will not only kill a small animal but it might kill a small boy, any of your companions, or yourself."

Papa bought a ranch near town and soon we had a lot of birds eating our crops. My Uncle J. R., who lived in South Pasadena, gave us an old ten gauge shotgun. That was a pretty big gun for boys to use and neither my brother Jesse nor I were prepared to shoot a shotgun.

The first time Jesse shot it, he was holding it out in front of him and he pulled both triggers at one time. A ten gauge shotgun with one barrel discharging has quite a kick. With two barrels discharging at one time, the wallop is tremendous. The butt of the gun crashed into Jesse's nose. Fortunately there was a thick soft rubber plate on the butt and no permanent damage was done to his nose even though it looked terrible for a long time. I noticed the next time he shot the gun, he put the butt up against a tree. I always held the gun close to my shoulder and tried to travel with the kick that came from its discharge.

We killed a lot of rodents, birds and animals and managed to save most of our crop. We used this old number ten gauge shotgun for many years and took it to college with us.

One time the drama we were producing called for a cannon outside on the street and we brought along the old number 10. We removed the shot from the shells and replaced them with wads. The effect was tremendous. The play was given both on Friday and Saturday evenings. The following Sunday morning there was a flock of birds outside our dormitory room situated on the second floor. They were making a lot of noise in the old oak tree there and keeping us awake, so I got the shotgun and threw in a couple of shells. I went to the window and pulled the trigger on the left barrel. The birds disappeared. I do not know whether I killed any or not for I looked down the gun and saw a piece of the barrel about six inches wide sticking out of the side of the gun. Apparently, one of the wads from the night before was left in the muzzle of the gun and the force of the explosion blew out this section of the barrel about four inches from the muzzle.

We took the gun home and had ten inches cut off the barrels. It was no good for hunting now so we left it home at Mama's request. In a few weeks Uncle J. R. wrote asking for the return of the gun. "I need it for a riot gun in case I am ever called out on any special duty."

He was no longer connected with the Los Angeles County Sheriff's Office, but was a highly regarded member of the County Health Department. I could not figure out just why he would need a riot gun. I guess he thought perhaps we did not know how to take care of a good shotgun or perhaps he was afraid we would get hurt.

That was the last shotgun I used for a long time. I heard and saw plenty of shooting in World War I and have not cared too much for guns since.

One of our favorite swimming places was on the Brown Ranch. Mr. Brown owned a large reservoir with water supplied by a deep well pumped by a big electric motor.

Mr. Brown raised many kinds of fruit—prunes, plums, nectarines, peaches, apricots and pears. During the fruit cutting season the whole family except Papa got up early in the morning and drove about two miles to the Brown Ranch.

Jesse drove the two horse team hitched to a low truck which hauled the fruit in from the field. Mama and Big Sis cut fruit and Bunny and I just helped part of the time, and part of the time we played. We quickly learned which places were off limits and never got into serious trouble. As I got older I was allowed to pick fruit.

The nicest people in town drove out to help Mr. Brown get his fruit dried. Families of doctors, lawyers, preacher, and school teachers all pitched in to take care of the ripening fruit. There was as yet no imported labor to do such work, so these many friends helped harvest the crop. As they cut the fruit and spread it on drying trays, they sang popular songs or hymns, or told funny stories. Fruit cutting was just like a picnic.

Several times during the day, someone would sprinkle the ground around the open sided cutting shed to keep down the dust and keep the air cooler.

After the fruit was all cut, about five o'clock, we all slipped into our swim suits and went down to the big reservoir for a swim, shouting and singing and having a glorious time together. Mr. Brown never wore a bathing suit. He simply dove into the water in his shirt and overalls. He came up, seized a bar of soap, soaped his garments thoroughly and then swam. After his swim, he walked back to the house in his wet clothes, put on a dry shirt and overalls and hung the wet garments up to dry.

"This is a good way to remove the sticky fruit from my clothes"; he said, "it saves my wife a great deal of work."

Mama did not allow us to go in with our clothes on.

Several years later I was big enough to drive the truck and Jesse was working in town during the summer. On the very hottest days on the way back to the orchard from the shed, I would take off my shoes and jump into the reservoir to cool off. It felt good.

I was still quite small when I decided I was big enough to pick peaches.

Picking peaches was simple, for a man came along with a big pole and shook the fruit off the trees and all you had to do was to pick it up and put it in a pail. When the pail was full you dumped the fruit into a box. You were paid by the box—five or six cents. Sometimes the fruit fell on a big piece of canvas spread under the tree and often there were no canvases and you picked fruit out of the dust. This was dirty work.

The second day I picked peaches off the ground, a bee stung me on the forearm. A man who was a tree shaker, spit a big wad of chewing tobacco into his hand and pressed it against my sting.

"Get that dirty tobacco off my arm," I squirmed, but he held me firmly, so I subsided as he explained that tobacco would extract the poison. It really did help.

I told Mama about my experience that night and she commented, "Well I'm glad to learn that tobacco is really good for something."

The first time I ever earned a whole dollar in one day was on a neighboring ranch picking prunes. At half past five I was still picking and had one more five cent box to fill to make a dollar. I always remember my friend who helped me finish that last box so that I earned a whole dollar. I was slow and small and he was quick and older.

When I grew older, I was invited to board on the Brown ranch during the summer for I had learned to milk a cow. Mr. Brown had two cows and he disliked milking. For milking his cows I received my room and board which I liked immensely because Mrs. Brown was a wonderful cook.

Two neighbor boys also ate lunch there.

We generally weighed on the scales at the cutting shed before and after we ate to see how much we could gain. The food was delicious—all kinds of vegetables, fresh and cooked, lots of good meat, plenty of cold ice tea, and watermelon for dessert. The most I could gain was seven pounds. The two neighbor boys could gain as much as eight or nine pounds at a meal, but with my best efforts I could never equal their gain.

They ribbed me quite a bit and one day I said, "I'll bet I can gain ten pounds between the time I come to work in the morning and noon." So they took up my bet.

From each load of peaches I brought in from the orchard, I would reach back and pick out one of the largest and juicest. As each load was stacked at the cutting shed, I continued to eat the largest fruit and drink lots of water. By twelve o'clock I had increased my weight by ten and a half pounds and so won my wager. I did not care for lunch that day.

Mr. Brown's brother-in-law told me about a little pig that got into his dried apricots and ate all the apricots he could hold, and then went to the canal and drank lots of water. He explained to me that the little pig burst his stomach right down the middle. I felt much the same way.

My favorite dried fruit was nectarines, especially the soft, sweet delicious white nectarines. At the end of the season, I bought a hundred pounds and took them home with me. Our family used nectarines for quite awhile and I'm sure Mama gave away quite a lot when I was not around.

When I was older, I was allowed to work in the prunes. Prunes were dried with the seeds left in. As they were brought from the orchard, they were dumped into a big wire basket and dipped into a solution of hot lye water. This cracked their skins so they dried well. On the Brown ranch they were dried in the hot sun on trays after they came out of the hot bath. After a couple of weeks they were turned over so they would dry thoroughly on both sides and then put into big boxes to sweat so that the moisture would be uniform throughout. Prunes were not worth very much in those days and I can remember lots of years they were sold from one to two cents a pound.

Lots of red, ripe, juicy watermelons grew in the fields on everybody's farms. My dearest friends had four or five acres of them and our great delight would be to walk out in the fields early in the morning, cut a melon open lengthwise, and eat only the heart. Sometimes melons would taste better if we got them from somebody else's patch. We never were caught getting them from anyone's patch although I'm sure that sometimes other farmers knew that we did take them. I suppose there were plenty because they were not worth much on the market. The only time I was ever ashamed of stealing them was when I went out with some boys in a buggy a couple of times between Sunday School and church on Sunday and got eight or nine melons from a man's patch.

My earliest recollections of watermelons in Tulare was driving in a buggy out to a farm and seeing the owner and his big boy load melons on to a big hayrack, drive out into a field where there were a lot of hogs and throw the melons to the hogs. The melons burst into pieces as they hit the ground. These hogs seemed to love them, but my feelings were sorely injured as I watched the hogs eat up all the melons. I felt better when the owner gave us a couple of big melons to take home with us.

Ice cold watermelon tasted best on a hot day, especially if you could sit in somebody's back yard and eat it without fork or spoon and just spit out the seeds. Sometimes we ate so much that our stomachs hurt something fierce if anyone told a joke and made us laugh. But we just kept on eating and laughing and aching because we loved watermelon so much.

There were still only a few automobiles driving up and down the dusty roads around Tulare. The father of one of my friends bought an E.M.F. I don't know what the initials stood for, but most everybody said they meant "every morning fixum." Anyway the car would stop occasionally very suddenly and they had to get a mechanic to fix it. My friend tried to teach my sister Bunny how to drive. We were with her one day out in the country when she became confused and turned the wheel the wrong way. We found ourselves right side up in a ditch. Mama would not let her drive after that, she thought she was too young. And I guess she was.

We were always having parties at our house and if

there were no parties in town, we always had one at our house on Friday night. Sometimes we didn't have much in the way of refreshments but Mama always provided plenty of fresh fruit or raisins and nuts, and things that people ought to eat instead of candy. Bunny was a great party planner and saw to it that we had lots of parties.

In our living room there two pianos, one an old square Emerson, an antique even then but we kept it for its beautiful case and sweet tone. The other piano was an upright and sometimes we had double duets on the pianos.

One of Bunny's friends used to come over to our house to play the piano. We tried to get him to play the Emerson only for when he played the upright he hit the keys so hard that the piano would seem to bounce up and down and would gradually move across the hardwood floor. We did not have many rugs. I guess we were too poor. And so there were no rugs to stop its progress. Frequently Papa used to sit and watch the piano move. He said he sometimes wondered how long it would take for the piano to move out the front door. I guess there was so much noise, occasionally he wished both pianos would move out the front door. The Emerson was too big, it could not have gone through the front door so Papa did not bet on that one.

There were no permanent buildings in Giant Forest when we first started going there to camp among the big redwoods. So we generally camped behind some huge fallen monarch and only an occasional deer, bear or skunk visited us. Few restrictions hampered us and our friends as we roamed and played in the woods.

Roads going into Giant Forest were poor—quite unlike

today's modern highways. The only dusty dirt road ran up the north fork of the Kaweah River by the Old Colony Mill. This steep road caused cars to boil and every car went up in low gear. Fully half the old Model T Fords wore out their bands driving in and their drivers were afraid to drive them out. There was no garage at Giant Forest, but Jesse and one of his friends capitalized on this situation by contracting to drive out the cars with no brakes.

The boys cut a tree and tied it to the rear of the disabled car and drove down the mountain road, while the owner generally rode the stage out. The stage driver was a good friend, so Jesse always rode the stage back to camp. I was sorry I was not big enough to engage in this profitable enterprise.

Chapter XIII

TRAMPS AND OTHER PEOPLE

Two big trees grew outside the white picket fence in front of our house in Tulare. Although the house was three blocks from the main railroad, tramps started coming to our house from the day we moved in.

Warm-hearted Mama never refused aid to a needy person, but she was also thrifty. Whenever a tramp came to our house begging for food she was ready to feed him, provided he earned his food.

Not so with Papa. He gave to the needy in the same generosity, but he believed that most tramps were just bums who did not want to work.

"I wonder," he mused, "if this house is marked in some way which directs tramps here."

So he asked Jesse and me to paint the front picket fence to eradicate any markings, but the tramps kept right on coming. We took out one of the big trees, but still the tramps came. Finally the second tree came out, and eventually the fence was taken down. Still the tramps. Papa decided that he could not win unless we moved, for the house seemed marked forever.

We burned wood in our kitchen stove and in our heaters for there was as yet no gas in Tulare. Big oak chunks went into the huge fireplace. Sometimes we bought only fireplace wood for it was cheaper and splitting it into stove size also provided exercise for boys and tramps.

When a tramp came to the back door asking for food Mama would say, "Go out there in the back yard and split some wood for half an hour and I'll give you a good breakfast."

If a tramp looked sickly or old or tired, Mama never let him work for more than a few minutes before calling him in to eat.

Some tramps did not want to work and would turn on their heels and leave. Others would start out toward the woodpile, pretending interest in work, but would pass on out through the back yard gate that conveniently led into the alley and go somewhere else looking for a soft touch.

For the tramps who did work, and many were hungry and wished to work, Mama cooked a good meal, serving it on the back porch steps. She never let any of them come into the house. Sometimes she would stop and talk to them a few minutes, but few wanted to talk and she left them alone. Some thanked her for their food and others never uttered a single word. Some were sensitive persons who were deeply appreciative of her kindliness. A few wanted to talk and unburdened their problems on Mama. She listened attentively.

"I would rather feed nine unworthy tramps," Mama repeatedly said, "than to turn away a single worthy one." For those who did not wish to work, Mama provided the easy means of escape—the back gate.

As long as Mama lived, she contiuned to feed tramps, but after a few years only the really hungry who wanted to work came to her door. I guess the rest of them heard about the wood pile.

141

Home from college during Christmas vacation, I had just slipped into my overcoat and was reaching for my hat when I heard a knock at the front door. The doorbell was out of order.

There stood a young negro tramp in tattered clothes, "Please suh, may I have a little food?"

"I'll see," for I was not sure Mama was still feeding tramps. So I turned back into the house and sought out Mama.

"Mama, there is a young negro tramp at the front door begging for food."

Now remember, Mama was a lady, a dignified southern lady. She hastened to the front door, flung it open, and addressed the ragged negro standing there. "You black nigger, what are you doing at my front door? Get around to the back door where you belong."

Tears burst from the young negro's eyes and coursed down his ebony cheeks. His tattered cap already in his hand, he threw in the air and fervently exclaimed, "Praise the Lawd, if I ain't found a southern lady."

He went to the back door. Mama prepared for him a special breakfast, even making fresh biscuits. He was not sent to the woodpile, but was brought into the warm kitchen on that cold morning.

I sat shamefacedly in the adjoining dining room listening through a crack in the door to the conversation as they discussed places in the south where they had both visited. You would have thought they were old friends. Mama recognized that here was a poor frightened negro boy who needed a friend. She sent him away with a big bag of Christmas goodies.

Mama had a warm understanding of negroes as many people raised in the north can never have. As a child she played with them. Her early life was spent helping them, so as negroes moved into Tulare to work in the newly developed cotton fields, they found in Mama someone who understood them and in whom they could find help in times of trouble. She spoke in their churches and comforted them in times of sorrow. In response they came to her door bearing gifts of fresh fruit and vegetables in season from their gardens. As long as Mama lived they continued to beat this path to her door in gratitude for her understanding and kindliness to them.

One old negro friend speaking about Mama after her death summed it up, "Your mother was the best friend a black man ever had in this town. She was always doing good for them. Helping with their children, helping when the old man got out of line, preaching in their churches, telling funny stories that make people laugh and be happy. Black folks sure gonna miss your Mama round this here town."

Hundreds of Chinese were employed on the big ranches where Papa looked after the office. Jesse and I found great delight in visiting the headquarters ranch and we became acquainted with many Chinese there.

Some of them camped on a section of the ranch in little huts and hovels which they had built with their own hands from scrap materials of all sorts. Others roomed and boarded in the big ranch dormitory and ate their meals in the big dining room.

These Chinese had come to America to work and make their fortune, but they were forced to leave their families in China. They must have missed their children for they were especially nice to Jesse and me.

Our special friends were the Chinese cooks, and when we visited the ranch we generally went to the kitchen about three or four o'clock in the afternoon for we knew they had finished the pies and cakes by that time. Sure enough we always received large portions of pie or cake or some other favorite dessert. Then our Chinese friends would tell us about their families in far away China and how soon they would return to them when they got lots of money. Sometimes they gave us presents of candy or cakes or lichee nuts, and around Chinese New Year many packages of red firecrackers.

In summer Jesse and I often drove early to the Paige Ranch to pick up Papa. There were so many interesting things to do there—fruit trees of all kinds to climb and ripe fruit to sample; bats to poke out of the rafters in the large driers. We took some home for pets once, but Mama objected; she said they were covered with fleas. Often we searched among the vines for the largest bunches, then each would sit in the shade and eat his entire bunch. Sometimes we were not hungry at supper, but those seedless grapes were delicious.

There were no super markets in those days and stores sold few vegetables, but most people bought from the peddlers who came to the door. Our best vegetables came from Wing Soo, one of our Chinese friends. Twice a week he drove the light spring wagon drawn by two horses to our front door and bargained with Mama for his beautiful fresh vegetables and fruit.

Wing Soo's visits were a source of joy and amusement for us. If Mama did not have cash to pay him on the spot it did not seem to make any difference since everyone did business on a credit basis. We never saw him write anything down, but he never disagreed with Mama about the amount of the bill owed. True, sometimes he would bring out his strange abacus if the accounting became too involved.

Soo brought us presents throughout the year, but he was most generous at Chinese New Year with his gifts of lichee nuts, firecrackers and candy. There were all kinds of candy—cocoanut, ginger, melon, and one kind that may have been flavored with ants. Another candy tasted like Pears' Soap.

Pears' Soap did not taste like pears at all, but was a brand of soap named for Mr. Pear, the manufacturer. Anyway this particular candy tasted like this brand of soap, and we didn't like the taste of it, so we traded it off for most anything of value, or no value, to our friends.

The firecrackers we enjoyed most of all, for they were noisy Chinese crackers and we would light a bunch at a time and run far away from the noise. Mama was always glad when we exhausted our supply of firecrackers for even though we were careful, she knew we might be injured.

Sometimes Mama would serve Wing Soo a cup of tea when he carried the vegetables into the kitchen, and he often presented her with a gift of a package of his favorite Chinese tea.

One morning Soo made Mama very angry. When he brought the vegetables to the kitchen, he saw the teapot on the warming hood of the big wood stove. Little Sis was sick the night before and Mama had not yet washed the teapot used at the evening meal. Soo said, "Oh, tea," and picking up Mama's teapot placed the spout in his mouth he drank long and generously.

Mama was furious. "What do you mean taking my

teapot and drinking from it. Why didn't you ask for a cup?"

"Oh, tea is much better this way." he replied. When he saw that Mama was really angry, he apologized and explained that this was his favorite way of drinking tea at home, and that he was carried away when he saw the teapot there on the stove.

"I like tea very strong. I thought tea on the stove very good." Maybe he was inferring that Mama did not make tea strong enough.

Wing Soo delivered vegetables to our house for three years and finally made enough money so he could go back to China and live in prosperity for the remainder of his life. I guess that was before inflation.

When we moved back into Tulare, we found that many Chinese lived in a certain section known as Chinatown. We became well acquainted with some of them and a few became close friends. Chinese children attended classes with us in our schools and were among some of our best scholars and finest athletes. One of these friends and his sister later became internationally famous as professional skaters.

We did not have much money when I attended high school, so generally after a basketball game at night we dropped into a Chinese restaurant operated by one of our friends. Here for a few cents we could enjoy a satisfying bowl of noodles and a soy sauce. We generally referred to soy sauce as "bug juice," for a good reason.

During the big floods in the Tulare Lake region huge beetles swarmed under the newly installed arc lights at the street intersections in Tulare. Chinese gathered these beetles and carried them carefully away to their homes.

One day I asked my Chinese friend, "What do Chinese do with beetles you so carefully pick up?"

"Oh, we mash 'em up. Make bug juice."

I did not use soy sauce for some time afterwards. Later I learned that the Chinese do really eat the beetles. At a banquet where this delicacy is served, one picks the beetle up carefully and pops it in the mouth. "Crush it immediately or the beetle wins and you will never get it down," explained my friend.

I never cared to try the morsel, although generally I was quite fond of Chinese dishes.

Some of my friends even enjoyed the good food that the Chinese placed on the graves of their departed.

They discovered that the food placed on graves was generally eaten by dogs, cats or some wild animal, and this seemed to please the mourners who thought that the gods had come and enjoyed the food. This insured a safe journey for the departed.

The food placed on the graves was the very best food and the boys thought is was a shame that such fine food should be wasted on dogs and cats, so sometimes they would slip out to a new grave at night before the cats and dogs, and have a good feed. They always left enough for the Chinese gods, and to satisfy the evil spirits. They said the food was delicious and did them a lot more good than it would the cats and dogs. They helped keep the friends of the departed happy.

When Mama heard about the escapades, she asked me not to eat any food from Chinese graves, so I never did.

Chapter XIV

FIRES, FLOODS AND CYCLONES

The most beautiful sight in all the world to small children was fire at night burning off the hills of the Sierra Nevada mountains. The fire was miles away but the contours and elevations of the burning hills etched fantastic patterns in the black of night. No fire-works ever equaled this display as the flames crept slowly toward the summit.

Conflict raged every year between those who wanted this undergrowth burned off the hills and those who believed that the brush prevented corrosion. The stockmen who ran cattle on the hills claimed that burning produced better grass the next spring. The conservationists stated that eventually the good soil would be washed away and no grass would grow.

By day the hill fires were but a distant cloud of smoke obstructing our view of the majestic mountains. We wished for night so we could see our lovely fire patterns.

Because we loved to see these forest fires by night, we were not aware of the danger.

Once we were camped in the mountains, when a fire broke out below us on the only exit road. Alarm spread through the camp and most of the children as well as the parents were in tears—from the smoke.

Mama spoke to us calmly and told us how people

148

saved themselves from forest fires by getting under water, "If the fire comes closer we will go up to the lake and get in the water up to our chins There are no big trees near the lake and we will be safe.

"If it gets too hot we will duck our heads under the water," she continued, "coming up only for air. I will show you how to keep safe and cool. There is no cause for worry."

We walked over to the lake but did not enter the cold water. Mama told us stories while we waited and after about two hours the fire was under control and danger passed.

Burning forests were not the only fires we knew for lots of houses and barns burned to the ground in Tulare.

In the early days Tulare was a shipping point for hay, grain and other agricultural products and huge warehouses lined the railroad spurs. A dozen or more enormous barns housed the teams hauling hay and grain from distant ranches to the warehouses. There were as yet no trucks nor were there paved roads.

In the dead of night the chilling din of fire sirens and bells awakened us to danger as our meager fire equipment tried to save the dry old wooden structures filled with loose dry hay. Often these big stables housed twenty to thirty horses and it was impossible to get them all out of the burning barn. Horses became frightened at the smell of smoke and the sight of fire, often they refused to budge from their stalls and occasionally one would run back into the burning building. In all of these fires two or more horses perished. To our young minds this was awful and gruesome.

Some people thought a "fire-bug" deliberately set fire to these barns. One man claimed he saw a man light a match and hold it to dry hay and run away, but no one was ever caught. Other people believed that careless smokers were responsible.

Once or twice our family slept through a big fire, and were quite chagrined the next day when everyone at school was talking about the excitement. Most of the time we piled out of bed at the first alarm and hurried into our clothes so we could see the fire at close range. People made so much noise we could never understand how we could have slept through a fire. Generally Papa went to the fire with us, but after we were older he preferred to stay at home. He was not a fireman.

Tulare burned to the ground on two previous occasions and the inhabitants were afraid of fire even though there was now adequate water and a good fire department. No fire department could have extinguished one of those old barns after it was in flames.

Houses burned too—sometimes to the ground, but most of them were saved—partly anyway. None of the big barns could be saved and the firemen turned the water on adjacent buildings and always saved them.

Once we were standing watching the flames whipping the black sky. Near us was a man—quite bald. A cinder floated down on his bald head.

He grabbed the top of his head, "My God! I'm on fire!"

He ran to an old horse trough a block away and submerged his head. Everybody laughed and forgot the fire for a moment.

One cold windy afternoon while I attended Pomona College, fire broke out in the mountains six miles north of Claremont between San Dimas and San Antonio Conyons. It was soon out of control and the fire-fighters

150

issued a call for more help. They particularly pled for college students to help.

It was Sunday afternoon and lots of us volunteered. "We will show them how to put out a fire in a hurry," we said. None of us had ever fought a forest fire, and we were going for a lark.

First they loaded us on trucks and rushed us up San Antonio Canyon. After a fifty minute hike, they decided that we could not get to the fire from that side so they rushed us back south around the hills to Palmer Canyon and we were on the firing line by four o'clock that afternoon.

There was little we could do because the strong wind made fire-fighting hazardous and the air was filled with sand and dirt. A pick or shovel was issued to each of us and we moved along after the fire, extinguishing embers which might blow back and start new fires further south of us.

After dark a detachment of twelve of fifteen of us under the leadership of a forest ranger moved down into a canyon to extinguish some embers which had blown into a clump of young pines. We just about had the flames extinguished when our leader looked up and saw that the wind had turned. Fire was now leaping across from crown to crown in nearby big pines.

Our leader did not hesitate. "Drop your tools," he yelled, "and run for your lives."

He led the way as we rushed down the mountainside tearing our clothes and our skin on burned manzanita and other undergrowth.

We did not realize at the time how serious our situation had been. Since then I have read of fire-fighters being trapped and burned to death in just such a situation. Over fifty amateur fire-fighters perished at one time under similar circumstances. We were fortunate to have had so wise a leader.

The heat from the fire was unbearable when we were near and we suffered from the intense cold when away from it. Drinking water was abundant but food was absent.

About eight o'clock a burro brought in a load of canned food. My ration was a can of peaches. A man near me received a can of pumpkin.

His eyes were full of sand and through the slits he squinted at the label. "Pumpkin," he said with an oath, and heaved can and contents down the canyon. I shared my peaches with him.

About midnight we were brought a huge kettle of steaks. They were cold but they tasted good even though well seasoned with dirt and sand driven under the lid by the violent gusts of wind.

Daybreak came soon and we were back on the line trying to extinguish embers and clean up bad spots. By noon my eyes were so full of dirt and sand and swollen that I was no longer able to open them. I could not see what I was doing, so I was ignominiously led back down the canyon, loaded on a truck with others and taken back to a doctor in Claremont.

When I returned to the dormitory I was told the the telephone operator was trying to reach me all morning. Soon they had Mama on the line. She did not know about the fire. She just wanted to know how I was. I did not tell her about the fire and my part in it, but when I wrote to her and Papa about my experience, she replied, "You were brave to volunteer to fight the fire. I thank God that you were under the leadership of so wise a man who knew when to run instead of staying there to fight and perish.

"I thank God daily for his loving care over each of us."

Years later Bunny, who still lived at home, told me the story.

About the time of night we were fleeing from the fire, Mama awoke with a start and awoke Papa, "Son is in trouble. He is in danger."

Papa tried to reassure her, "You've just had a bad dream."

"No," she replied, "it was clear and real to me."

She mentioned this experience at breakfast and talked to Papa again. Then she decided to phone me.

Some people seem to have keener perceptions than others. Mama seemed to have an extra sense and understanding, especially she was extra wise about her children and Papa.

Bad floods shut off all communications around Claremont one year. Even the phones were out for a day.

Heavy rains in the mountains brought high water down the mountain sides. Streams could not contain the floods and their water sought new channels. San Antonio Creek to the east and San Gabriel River farther to the west overflowed their banks and rolling boulders took all bridges before them. All railroads and highways were shut off.

No flood control dams held back the water and it spread where it willed. One stream even ran across the Pomona College campus as rolling rocks filled old stream beds and the dirty swirling water sought new outlets. Our only outside contact was with Pomona City—four miles away.

Los Angeles daily newspapers carried the story and suggested food shortages in the isolated area if some bridges could not soon be repaired.

Mama phoned the second day for she had read the papers, "Are you getting enough to eat?" she asked.

We had not seen a city paper for two days and were not aware of food shortages.

"We're eating a lot because of the rain and floods," Jesse told her and "we have been tramping lots to see all the floods."

"I hope son, that you are not trying to stop them."

"No Mama, they're too big for anybody to stop. We are just looking." He promised not to do anything rash.

When we were small children in Tulare we enjoyed the floods. They were most gentle compared to the Southern California mountain streams, but every spring as snows melted in the Sierra Nevadas the streams and irrigation ditches overflowed their banks.

Tulare was built on high ground and all flood waters passed around, but nearby towns of Visalia and Porterville were on streams and sometimes seriously damaged. The damage around Tulare was to farm lands only.

Some years damage to crops was slight, other years vast acreage was flooded and loss was great. The greatest loss was in the old Tulare Lake bottom.

Years ago Tulare Lake was a sizeable body of water probably thirty or forty miles long and at least twenty miles wide. It was not deep but excursion boats carried passengers on outings and winds whipped up bad storms on its surface. As more and more water was diverted for irrigation of dry lands from streams that fed the lake, the lake itself began to dry up and the fertile land was reclaimed for agriculture. Huge dikes

154

twenty or more feet high were built around the lake and across certain portions of the old bed. Enormous pumps lifted surplus water over levees to unused sections, so that the dry sections could be planted in barley and wheat.

Some years the entire lake bed was dry and farmable, but wet years or a series of wet years might overflow the levees and flood all the farm land. At one time the water extended beyond the levees almost to the original shores of the lake.

One summer Mama and I drove down to see the high water. We passed down through the town of Corcoran about a mile and came to a hastily erected levee blocking the concrete road we travelled. We climbed up on the levee and saw houses, barns and farms under water. Thousands of bales of hay floated on the water. These farmers are glad now that flood control dams up the stream and prevents reoccurrence of this sort of disaster.

Too much water was the big hazard of farming in the lake bottom, but the big crops that the fertile land produced more than offset the financial losses.

As small children we liked the little floods best. As the water rushed down from the mountains, it filled the streams and the big ditches and then the little ditches and flowed out over the land and sometimes the roads. It was not deep and did little harm.

With every creek full and every ditch running over in the spring it was time for swimming again and we were off to our favorite swimming holes. No life-guards watched over us and generally no parents were present, but we never heard of anyone drowning. We were taught to be careful of water.

I learned to swim by being thrown into the water,

but the boys who threw me in were careful to see that I got along all right with my dog paddling.

For a few years we owned a ranch near Tulare. One summer the flood tore through our ranch and ruined a lot of hay. At one time an old creek had coursed through our place, but now it was filled in and cultivated both on our ranch and the place below us. The old creek bed had never been filled in above us, so when the high water came above us it flowed into this old stream and flooded our hay in the low places.

One November day the rain came down in torrents. Rain was usually welcome in dry country like Tulare, but this rain changed suddenly into hail and the hail kept getting bigger and bigger and soon pieces over an inch in diameter were knocking off flowers and leaves and fruit. Our lawn and yard and all the streets were covered with hail.

The sudden change in temperature caused a cyclone south of town which whisked away some barns and sheds, but no one was injured. Everyone was excited for that was the only cyclone anyone had ever seen near Tulare.

Chapter XV

TULARE PROGRESSES

When we first disembarked from the train in Tulare, we were impressed by the beautiful park. In one end was a big drinking fountain where the thirsty could drink of the cool pure water, but most of the people in the park were rough looking characters. We learned that they did not care for the water. People called drunks or "winos". They got their drinks across the street in one of the fourteen saloons which ranged almost side by side in a single block. Many of the men begged for money as you walked by; others worked occasionally in the fruit or hay to get a few dollars so they could buy some more cheap wine.

We were never allowed to play in this park unless Papa and Mama were both with us, but the butcher shop where we bought our meat was right in the middle of the block of saloons, so sometimes we could get a peek through the doors which constantly swung open.

Two of the saloons boasted rear doors called "Family Entrances" through which women, they were not called ladies, could enter for a drink. Why they were called "Family Entrances" I never learned, for I never saw any families enter from the alleys. All women must enter only through alley entrances and ladies did not enter saloons.

One day when I was returning from the meat market

a man held the swinging saloon door open as he shouted to someone inside. I got a good look and saw a woman drinking at the bar. At supper that night I said, "Papa, I saw a lady drinking at the bar in a saloon this afternoon."

"If you saw a woman drinking in a saloon, you can be sure she was no lady. She was probably a prostitute," Papa replied.

"What is a prostitute?" I asked.

Mama broke in, "We will discuss that later." I learned years later that they were bad women who lived in the redlight district over beyond Chinatown. Most people referred to them as whores.

A small canal ran along the edge of this section. One day as we drove by, little Bunny saw a bright orange bridge and rails extending over this canal connecting a house with the street. The door of the house was bright red. "Pretty, pretty," Bunny exclaimed. "Pretty house."

"That's a house of ill-fame," Papa explained.

"What's the matter with its frame? It seems to be standing all right." I questioned.

Papa replied, "Never mind." So I knew it was something I should not discuss.

A few years later the redlight district was banished along with the saloons.

Almost every day brawling and fighting erupted on Front Street among the drunks congregated there. Mama would not permit my sisters to walk on this street. One day there was a big fight in one of the saloons and the city marshal came in to stop it. One of the drunks shot him. He died the next day and there was lots of bitter feeling in the town for the marshal was quite popular and the man who shot him was "just a drunk," everybody said. Some people talked about lynching. Others said, "Oh, he was too drunk to know what he was doing. He should be allowed to go free."

Some people decided that these saloons did not do the town any good and so they started a movement to eliminate them. Mama became very active in the work in the W.C.T.U. and became one of their leaders in the Loyal Temperance Legion group. All of our family belonged to the L.T.L. and we learned all their songs and signed their pledges.

The songs all had lively tunes and dealt with the evils of alcohol. One song especially we sang with feeling.

> "We're coming. We're coming
> A brave little band
> On the safe side of temperence
> We will now take our stand.
> We don't use tobacco
> Do you know what we think,
> That the boys who will use it
> Are quite sure to drink."

Boy Scouts, Girl Scouts, Campfire Girls and all the others youth organizations were not yet invented. Aside from church programs, there was only the Boys Brigade. The LTL finally took all of its members and the Brigade folded, and its members were soon working for the elimination of saloons.

Such enthusiasm cannot be denied, consequently a few years later the citizens of Tulare voted to throw out the saloons and Tulare was a dry town until the end of the great prohibition era when control of saloons became a state responsibility.

Mama became an ardent worker for the WCTU and

LTL and was soon elected to state office. She was a forceful speaker and in demand all over the state. Her talks were humorous and inspiring. Most of her humorous stories Papa made up from stories he read in newspapers or magazines. He could take a single line and make a humorous story. Papa was not the talking type for he was known as a quiet man, but he did speak well and forcefully. Whenever he rose to his feet to speak, everyone listened because they knew he had something important to say.

Tulare was beautiful but almost dead when we moved there in the spring of 1899. The Southern Pacific Railway shops, which played so important a part in its economy, had just been moved to Bakersfield. Prices for agricultural crops were extremely low. The Southern Pacific Railway dominated the state legislature and charged exorbitant freight rates for hauling grain and other products to city markets in San Francisco and Los Angeles. The Tulare Irrigation District was unable to meet its bond obligations and the community's financial rating was almost nil.

Finally some of the community leaders decided to do something about the situation. They went to San Francisco and talked to the irrigation bond holders, "Look. Tulare is broke and dead. If things go the way they are you will receive nothing on your bonds. We believe that individuals in our community can raise fifty cents on the dollar and pay you that amount for your bonds. We believe that if something like this is not done the financial rating of Tulare will worsen."

At first the bond holders were not receptive to the proposal but finally concluded that perhaps fifty cents on the dollar was better than nothing. "Can you assure us that the people of Tulare can raise this money? Can you consummate this payment within six months?"

"You have only our word that we will try. We have great faith in our community and our people."

Next was the money raising. Banks gave generously since they felt their future was closely connected with the success of the undertaking. Public meetings brought large subscriptions from the wealthy. The poor even reached into their meager savings and donated to their future. By the end of six months the full amount was in the banks. The bonds were redeemed and brought to Tulare.

A public bond burning and celebration date was set. The governor was invited to speak and preparation progressed for a barbecue with music, festival and dancing.

Huge barbecue pits dug in the park contained numerous beef, pigs, and lambs basting over the coals. While the fragrant odor of roasting meat permeated the air, the governor spoke commending the community for its successful effort, the bonds were burned in a huge wire basket. My sisters sang in the musical part of the the program, but Jesse and I just sat smelling that good meat and hoping the program would finish soon so we could eat.

After the feast competitive sports and dancing occupied the afternoon. I could not run very fast I had eaten so much.

No one could climb the greased pole until one boy filled his pockets with sand and dirt. He applied this freely to the pole as he climbed and finally reached the top.

A big boy finally caught the greased pig. So many

boys tried to catch the poor pig, I think they had rubbed off most of the grease by the time the pig was caught.

After the bonds were burned, Tulare prospered and in time enjoyed improvements of electric lights, gas, sewers, paved streets and sidewalks.

I was glad to have electricity for I was the one in our family, it seemed to me, who always had the job of filling the kerosene lamps and washing the chimneys. It was quite a chore getting a kerosene lamp chimney to shine to the proper degree.

We had all kinds of fancy kerosene lamps including our prize, a huge porcelain sphere painted with pink roses. After we installed electricity in our house we gave this beautiful lamp to one of our friends who lived far out in the country away from electricity. We kept one lamp, however, because sometimes the electricity went off. We were glad we did and wished we had kept more kerosene lamps because the sudden shut-off of electricity on many occasions left our home in darkness.

Mama kept a supply of wax candles on hand at strategic places so that we could have emergency light as needed.

All carriages had candles in the lamps attached to the sides. The lamps were not much help in seeing the road as you drove along, but they were good to indicate your presence to some other vehicle. They were open on the front and on the side. The lamps had a small red glass lens inserted in the back so that any team coming up from the rear would note your presence. The side of the lamps next to the occupants was solid metal and did not shine on the occupants. I was told it was arranged especially this way so that lovers out for a ride could exchange kisses and caresses. I cannot vouch for this because at the time I was not old enough to be interested in such things.

In the second decade of the century, a group of California men decided that the control of the California legislature by the Southern Pacific Railroad must be broken. The man who spear-headed this attack was a noted native of San Francisco. He decided to run for governor on a platform which would bring reform to transportation in California.

One night he and his opponent for the office of governor spoke in the old pavilion in Tulare. Hiram Johnson, for that was his name, was cheered roundly by the residents for they had felt the strangle hold of an unfriendly railroad for many years. They knew that if they could secure adequate transportation rates the community would surely prosper.

The victory of Hiram Johnson in this campaign and his subsequent establishment of adequate bureaus to control transportation in California are now a matter of history.

During Hiram Johnson's term of office many other reforms were initiated in California. The referendum, the recall, the initiative and other progressive measures which have strengthened the rights of the individual in our state.

Hiram Johnson went on to represent his state in the United States Senate. He was a favorite son of Tulareans for many years as he continued strong leadership for the rights of human beings.

Better transportation and better economic situations brought new prosperity to Tulare. There was also a change in crops, in methods of irrigation, and marketing procedures. Farmers began to grow alfalfa, excellent in the feeding of dairy cattle. Some progressive farmers drilled wells and water was pumped by gasoline engines which irrigated their alfalfa crops so that they were able to raise six or seven crops of hay a year. Most of these gasoline engines were replaced later by electricity for the people of Tulare county had formed an electric power company and generated electricity along mountain streams and distributed it to the consumers within the county. This brought electricity into our homes and lightened the work on the farms.

With the growing of alfalfa came the development of dairies. Soon Tulare had a creamery that made butter which was shipped to Los Angeles, and before long there were four or five creameries and milk processing plants in the community. Shipped to Los Angeles and San Francisco, besides butter, were fresh milk, cottage cheese, buttermilk and cream.

Many of the grain farms gave way to alfalfa and dairies, for dairies provided a continuous dependable product from the labor on the farm, and there was a ready market for dairy products.

Papa was office manager at the Paige Ranch for a number of years, but some of his friends who owned a big flour mill on the south end of town tried to persuade him to handle their office and supervise their sales. Papa had worked in Seattle with a milling company, and his friends felt he would help their business considerably. Papa finally agreed to work for them and so we decided to move to town.

Mama and Papa looked around for a new home and finally found a big old two story house situated about a half a mile from the flour mill and about one half a mile from the center of town. Mama borrowed some money from her brother, Uncle Bud, for the down payment and we moved in. The next few months Jesse and I were busy most of our spare time fixing up this house. We painted the outside with three coats of linseed oil and white lead. One of our friends loaned us high ladders and brushes. Mama and Big Sis, meanwhile, were repapering much of the inside and making the floors shine. We loved this home and lived in it for many years. Later we added two big screen porches for summer sleeping. Much later we installed two baths. When we moved there was no sewer system only a three hole chick sales in the back yard.

The people of the town finally voted sewer bonds. Small boys enjoyed watching the huge digging machines make deep cuts as the big sewer pipes were laid. The country around Tulare was flat, so the ditches were deep in order to provide sufficient flow. The one thing I remember most about this job was talking to the superintendent one day. He pointed to a man down in a ditch ten feet deep and said, "That man is worth ten times as much to me as any other man working on a shovel. I don't have to watch him, I don't have to tell him what to do, he will be promoted to a foreman's job." That statement impressed me greatly for here was a leader of men who talked the same way that Mama and Papa talked.

After Papa went to work for the Tulare Milling Company, he had more time to take me fishing. I liked this new job. Papa seldom came home from work that I didn't say, "Papa, let's go fishing."

Sometimes Papa would sigh, and we would go fishing. Other times Mama would speak up and say, "No, Papa is tired, you can go fishing some other day."

Another thing I liked about Papa's job was the chance to travel with him. About once a year he would take the train to nearby towns and call on customers to see how they liked the flours and other cereals which the milling company sold. To some of the out of way places, he would travel by horse and buggy, either renting a team and carriage from a local livery stable, or sometimes driving our horse and buggy. Most of the trips I took with Papa were the horse and buggy trips. Some of the country out toward Porterville was wild and barren. Occasionally, we had to ford a stream. Best of all was a chance to stay overnight with Papa in a hotel.

One of the owners of the milling company also owned a bakery. This bakery shop made all kinds of bread and pastries for there were no big bakeries delivering bread to the grocery store. Everyone in Tulare ate some of the bread, or pies, or cakes, or rolls from this bakery. I remember one man saying one day, "The Tulare bakery affects the lives of more people than any other force in the community. Some days the bread is good and some days its sour and gives people indigestion." I never had indigestion, so I could not understand until I got older.

Papa worked for the milling company for four or five years, but one windy night fire broke out on the fourth floor and the old dry wooden structure burned to the ground. The owners decided not to build so Papa was out of a job.

Papa decided that this rapidly growing community needed a first class job printing office. There were already two printing shops both conducted with newspapers, but neither of them, in Papa's opinion, produced the quality of job work that a good printer should. They were mostly interested in their subscriptions and newspaper advertising. So Papa secured a lease in a good location and bought presses, type, paper and all the necessary things that go into a good job printing office.

He continued to operate this business for many years, and Jesse and I helped him in the shop at times and Mama sometimes worked on his books or helped him with collections.

I thought I was a real sharp pressman and one Christmas I was home for vacation. I needed money as usual and was feeding envelopes by hand into a Chandler-Price press. An envelope missed the gauge pins and I threw off the impression lever. As I reached for the envelope to place it in proper place the impression release lever was loose and it bounced back as I stuck my hand down into the press. My entire right hand was crushed.

Papa was horrified because there had never been an accident in his office in the years that he had been in business. He hurried me down to see the old family physician. I was squeezing my right hand with my left and the blood was oozing out the end of my fingers.

Our doctor stood visiting at the foot of the stairs, which led to his office on the second floor. I said to him, "Doc, I have a little job here for you to patch me up."

He gave a quick glance at it and said, "Go on upstairs to the office and I'll be up there in a few minutes."

I was pretty angry for I felt that my wound needed his immediate attention. He patched me up in good shape though, and I lost a nail from my middle finger. Besides that everything grew back to normal in the course of years.

Every job turned out by Papa's office was both

artistic and of superior workmanship. Papa permitted no inferior work to be delivered. Soon firms all over the San Joaquin Valley were ordering job printing from his shop.

Papa actively participated in a movement to secure a new charter for Tulare, and helped establish the city as one of the first in California operating with a City Manager. A few years later the man who served as Clerk-Auditor for the city retired and the city council and many of Papa's friends asked him to accept appointment to this position. So Papa finally agreed to accept the position of responsibility with the city and sold his business to a young man who worked for him.

Papa served his city until his death years later and public officials held him the same high regard as did all his associates. When I was older I talked to representatives of bond companies and financial companies who were familar with Papa's work. They were unanimous in the opinion that there was no finer accounting and auditing system in any city than that established and maintained in Tulare by Papa.

Chapter XVI

A YEAR OF SORROW

Grandpa moved to Catalina Heights in Los Angeles in 1898 and preached every Sunday in the Presbyterian church nearby. His real estate office on Pico Boulevard was a busy place, but he was always present at the dedication of every new church in Southern California.

I rode with Grandpa in his new carriage out Pico Boulevard towards Santa Monica. Everything past Western Avenue was barley fields and farms, until we reached some of the small villages near Santa Monica.

Grandpa prospered in Catalina Heights as he prospered elsewhere, but he gave away his wealth for he was generous with his money and with his time. He preached in many other churches and listeners loved his humorous stories. He collected a huge store of stories about Texas and seemed to enjoy telling new acquaintances from Texas the most insulting of these. With the punch line, he threw his head back and roared.

As he grew older his hair became thinner and his hooked nose seemed larger, but his beard was always neatly trimmed and his blue eyes brimmed with mirth.

Grandpa was blessed by having a wife like Grandma. She adored him greatly, humored him, petted him, and provided him with wonderful meals for she did learn to cook and sew and iron and maintained a well-kept home. She read avidly and was perhaps even better informed that Grandpa. Her kindness, her patience, her consideration and encouragement helped him achieve his worthwhile deeds.

Grandpa still suffered from his war wounds and had to give up preaching regularly, but he never complained. He was jovial and good natured about everything, and dearly loved his family and his friends. Though his health was failing he was determined to die with his boots on.

"My only prayer about my health is that I may die with my boots on." He dreaded the thought of being bedfast.

He complained of not feeling well one night and retired early. Next morning he arose as usual and started to dress. He got his boots on and then lay back and went to sleep. He never awakened for he had joined his forefathers in the Great Beyond.

He died on August 8, 1903 and was interred in the Rosedale Cemetery. He left his mark on people and communities wherever he lived as he preached, taught, founded schools and colleges. He left hundreds of warm friends who mourned his passing, and felt the deep influence of his life.

After Grandpa Jonathan died, Grandma Belle continued to live on Catalina Street in Los Angeles. Aunt Buena and her husband, Uncle Harry, thought it was not good for her to be alone so they sold their house in Angelino Heights and built a home next door to Grandma, but she continued to live there by herself.

I liked to visit her. She still had Polly the parrot, and Polly was old now but still a great talker. Polly was particularly fond of crackers and cheese and when she woke up in the morning, she aroused Grandma with

her pleas, "Polly wants a cracker. Polly wants a cracker."
But for breakast Polly had to have her coffee also.

Polly was especially fond of cheese flavored with
coffee and Grandma would dip a piece of cheese in her
coffee and give it to Polly. This idea of flavoring cheese
with coffee appealed to me and Grandma would humor
me by melting cheese in her coffee. It was delicious,
and although I have grown older, I still enjoy cheese
melted in coffee.

Mama would say, "You have to be fond of cheese to
enjoy coffee with cheese flavor."

One year Grandma invited me to travel on the train
with her to Oregon to visit some relatives in Lebanon.
I joined her at Tulare and enjoyed an exciting trip. I
remembered especially Shasta Springs and the springs
by the railroad station at Ashland.

Grandma Belle told Mama she woke up from a nap
one time and I had the car window open and was sitting
in the window with my feet outside. I do not remember
the incident in that way. I may have been straddling
the window with one leg outside.

Grandma Belle never asked me to travel with her
to Oregon again. The next time she went up, she took
my sister Bunny with her. But she took Bunny only
once, too.

We visited in Grandma's old home in Lebanon. My
Aunt Bellroy now lived in a big house with her husband, Uncle Sam. Back of the house ran the beautiful
Santiam River. Lucious strawberries grew in the big
yard. So did kohlrabi, but I did not like kohlrabi.

We caught fish in the river, and at one time at the
table, I got a fish bone hung in my throat. Uncle Sam
picked me up by the heels and hung me upside down

171

while he patted me on the back. I thought he patted a little too hard and I did not like him very much at the time.

Grandma continued to live alone on Catalina Street, but after a few years moved over to Arcadia to live with her daughter, my Aunt Eunice. Aunt Eunice died suddenly with pneumonia. Meanwhile because of business connections, Aunt Buena and Uncle Harry had to sell their home and move to San Pedro. By this time, most of the children in our family were away at school or married so Mama invited Grandma to come up and live with her and Papa.

She was a sweet, frail, little old lady who persisted in frilly lace hankerchiefs and frilly lace collars. She carried Grandpa's huge gold watch on a black ribbon hung around her neck. In the back cover, on one side was a picture of Grandpa Jonathan opposite a picture of her first husband, Captain Lilly. Grandma confided to me, "I've been a very lucky woman. I've had two wonderful husbands."

Grandma became frailer each year. One early December morning, just before she was ninety, she did not come down for breakfast. She had died in her sleep.

Papa suffered for several years from angina pectoris and occasionally a severe attack would cause him intense pain. The doctor gave him little nitroglycerin tablets, which he carried in his vest pocket. He was happy and cheerful except when he had one of these attacks, which the nitroglycerin relieved immediately.

I visited Papa and Mama at Christmas during the same month that Grandma had passed away. My birthday, the day after Christmas ordinarily did not receive much attention after the big interest in Christmas. This particular year, Mama decided that she would have her Christmas dinner at noon on my birthday. I picked up Papa at his office and he took extra time for lunch as we enjoyed the wonderful food Mama had prepared. We sat around laughing and joking for half an hour after the meal.

I was to take Papa back to the office, but as we stepped onto the sidewalk to get into the car, he pitched forward over onto the grass.

He had departed this world.

Even though we had known for years that he would go this way, we were not prepared for this shock. Mama suffered most of all for she had lived with Papa during all of his illness and knew that the end would come this way.

The services were held in the old Congregational church and it was packed with friends and loved ones. Papa had few enemies and many warm friends. People who had learned to appreciate his good work and who loved him for the kindly assistance he had given them and who had enjoyed his ready wit and encouraging smile, filled the church or joined the overflow to pay their last respects.

By this time all of the children were married and each of us, in turn, tried to persuade Mama to come and live with us, but she rejected each invitation. Jesse lived only thirty miles away at Delano, and he occasionally dropped in to see her. The rest of us lived some distance and were unable to call on her as often as we would have liked.

I built a cottage for her on our property in Ventura and tried to persuade her to come and live with us, but she would never stay more than two weeks.

"No," she said, "here in Ventura I am just the Grandmother of your children. When I'm in Tulare, I have hundreds of young friends and they help me to keep young. Thank you for your invitation and I'll come to see you occasionally, but I want to keep the old home in Tulare."

During the spring after Papa and Grandma Belle died, Jesse had some rather serious attacks and local doctors seemed unable to properly diagnose the difficulty. During early summer, he attended a Rotary convention in New York and stopped off in Chicago to consult additional medical experts, but here again received conflicting diagnoses. One Saturday, in the middle of summer, he stopped off at our home in Ventura and told me about his troubles. I urged him not to delay any longer but to get into a noted Santa Barbara hospital for a complete check-up as soon as possible.

"I have already made arrangements," he said, "to come down here next Tuesday and enter the Santa Barbara hospital. I have a school board meeting Monday night and as soon as that is over, I'm coming down there and try to find out just what is the trouble."

He never lived to enter the Santa Barbara hospital.

Tuesday morning I was called from a summer school class at the University of Southern California to answer an urgent phone call.

My wife was on the phone, "Mama has received a phone call from Delano asking her to come up. Jesse has been taken to the hospital and was operated on."

She had already checked the bus service to Castaic Junction and I was to meet Mama there and drive her to Delano.

Mama was waiting when I arrived at Castaic Junction

and we proceeded over the mountains toward Delano as fast as an old model A Ford could travel. The speed on the down grade toward Bakersfield was limited slightly by the traffic laws in effect. The day was unbearably hot and the fan belt broke ten miles out of Bakersfield so we were delayed.

As the mechanic was fixing the fan belt Mama turned to me and said, "There is no need to hurry now, Son, for he is already dead."

'How do you know, Mama," I replied. "We must keep our faith."

"Yes, I know. We have our faith, but Jesse has already passed to the Great Beyond."

I was stunned by her attitude, but as we sped along again, I recalled how she knew by some divine message when I almost burned while fighting forest fire. I remembered the other times that she seemed to hold a direct communication with all her loved ones night and day. I pondered—was this some divine power she possessed or was it because of her noble capacity to love?

We drove to the home of Jesse's mother-in-law and met his wife Vera at the door. Mama said, "He is gone. We are too late."

"Yes. He's gone." Vera replied.

Memorial services were held at the Community Church in Delano. Great masses of flowers banked the front of the church. The church was crowded but a host of people stood without. Among them were hundreds of high school and college young people who had joined with adults to pay final tribute to this man they loved so much.

Chapter XVII

REGENERATION OF A SPIRIT

From the time of Jesse's affliction as a small boy Mama devoted her strength and all her energy to making him well again. We moved to California at Mama's insistence because the doctors thought the new climate would help him. She denied herself that he might have the best of medicine and care. Her purpose in life was to make Jesse strong and healthy.

How admirably did she succeed. Even though his lame leg was two inches shorter, Jesse had grown into vigorous, self-reliant happy manhood. He was just forty years old when he died.

In many ways Jesse was like his Grandfather Jonathan, with his high forehead, hooked nose, ready wit and hearty laugh, a twinkle in his eye, ready to tell a joke or hear a good one. As a successful high school principal and superintendent he had thousands of warm friends all over California and professionally was moving upward toward a more important position. In his good health and in his success, Mama's life seemed fulfilled.

Gramdma Belle died early in December. Papa passed away suddenly on the twenty seventh of the same month. Brother Jesse died swiftly the following June.

Mama seemed reconciled to the passing of Grandma Belle for she was nearly ninety years old and frail.

Mama grieved greatly at Papa's passing, but she knew for years that he would pass just this way. After Papa's first heart attack, Mama gave up all her state work with the WCTU and other organizations, so that she could be with Papa all the time. Although Papa continued his work at the city hall, Mama drove him back and forth and gave him the same loving care she had given Jesse when he needed it. Nothing can stop angina pectoris and Papa passed suddenly one afternoon.

No one was prepared for Jesse's passing. True, we all knew that he suffered from some undiagnosed ailment, but outwardly he seemed well and vigorous. Perhaps it was the three deaths in such a short period of time. It may have been the suddenness of Jesse's death but for a time we feared that Mama had given up completely and that she too wanted to die.

She seemed totally and completely crushed. Gone was her virgorous urge to do things. Gone was her cheerful greeting and her gracious smile. She wished to see no one nor to hear anyone. For the first time in her life she avoided people. Her great love for all people seemed departed from her.

She came to stay with us for a time in Ventura, but it was like having a stranger in the house for she was so different from the Mama we had known. She seemed possessed with a bitterness toward all people and doubt in the goodness of God.

The Scotch-Irish are known as a vigorous, brilliant, adventuresome race possessing a high degree of both stamina and stick-to-itiveness as well as moral integrity and leadership. No less that ten presidents of the United States could trace with pride their ancestry to the Scotch-Irish.

The impact of these people on our country has been widespread for when they came to America, they did not settle in a single colony as did many newcomers, but spread throughout the land and provided influence and leadership in many sections.

Most of the Scotch-Irish came originally from the lowlands of Scotland westward across the sea to the north of Ireland where they were later joined by Scotch Highlanders. Many of these emigrants left Scotland because of persecution, some sought adventure and others richer soil on which to raise their crops and flocks.

As new frontiers were developed in America, this restless group of people claimed rights in this new land and sought concessions from their king. The seven Kirkpatrick brothers secured a grant from King James and settled in what is now Mecklenburg County, North Carolina, below the city of Charlotte. Other Scotch-Irish groups from the North of Ireland secured grants in this area, and together provided the leadership and influence to make this section one of the strong points of revolt in both the Revolutionary War and the Civil War.

The famous Mecklenburg Declaration of Independence was signed here on May 20, 1775 over a year before the national Declaration of Independence. Many believe that the Mecklenburg document was the basis from which Thomas Jefferson worked out the final Declaration of Independence.

Lord Cornwallis, Commander of the British Army, named Charlotte "the hornet's nest" because of the annoying activities of the patriot troops during his occupancy of the city in 1780. The "war-devils" of Mecklenburg County never gave up and in engagement fought if necessary to the last man.

During the Civil War these people fought their brothers from the North with the same intensity and with willingness to die for their cause. They sincerely believed that their freedom was in jeopardy.

In Charlotte, Jefferson Davis held his last full cabinet meeting in 1865, and although many miles from the sea Charlotte was at one time designated as a Confederate navy yard.

Mecklenburg County was famous in peace as well as war. James Polk, eleventh President of the United States, was born there. Historically this region founded early academies and colleges, usually affiliated with the Presbyterian Church.

In America, as in Scotland and the North of Ireland, the Kirkpatrick clan was known as an honest, moral, courageous race possessing physical strength, a spirit of adventure, and a strong hatred of hypocrisy. These characteristics passed from generation to generation and dominated the lives of each member of the clan.

Mama was one of this clan.

My brother Jesse lived only thirty miles from our old home, so he tried to visit Mama more often after Papa died. After Jesse's death, although I lived two hundred miles distant, I felt responsible to phone Mama regularly and often she came to see us for a few days. One night I phoned to ask her to come down to see us, but she replied, "No, thank you, but I am too busy."

This was a sudden change from the depressed attitude she had maintained since Jesse's death, that I explained further, "Well we're coming up anyway to see you and we thought it would be nice if you returned with us."

"Look, son," she laughed, "you don't have to worry about me anymore. I'm all right now."

I was still worried and said, "Well, we'll be up anyway."

"Come on up. I'll be glad to see you all, but you can't persuade me to return with you. I have already explained that I am too busy."

I did not know just what she was busy doing, so I simply replied, "Well, we'll be up Friday night."

When we arrived in Tulare we learned that she had suddenly thrown herself into community betterment. She strongly renewed her participation in the work of her church, and especially with young people.

The next day she sat down with me for a serious talk. "I am entirely reconciled to the passing of your brother."

I just nodded and she continued, "I believe you know that I was quite bitter about his death in the prime of his life. I've prayed to my Maker and I have read my scripture that 'the Lord giveth and the Lord taketh away'. I'm going to stay in Tulare until I die and work for the benefit of the young people of this community, just as your father and your brother have done, while they lived here."

Sometimes we were able to persuade her to come to Ventura to visit for a few days, but a few days was all she would stay. She wanted to get back to her work and her young friends.

"Here in Ventura," she reminded me, "I am just the Grandmother of your children. In Tulare I have hundreds of young friends and people do not think of me as being old."

So she drove herself to do community and church work and she drove her car many miles transporting young people to the many meetings that young people must attend. I remonstrated for I felt that some younger woman or man could at least provide transportation and save her long out of town trips and grave responsibility, but she insisted that this, too, was a joy to her and she loved to do it.

She became the family counselor in her church and in her community serving without pay and I suspect that she gave away to the needy more than she should have from her own meager funds.

She continued to be in great demand as a speaker and seemed to acquire even greater facility and eloquence in delivery of a talk. Seldom was I able to hear any of her new talks, but friends told me of her success. Finally I was able to slip into an audience and hear her speak.

"Mama," I said after the meeting, "you certainly have developed a wonderful new ability to speak. I believe that was the best talk I ever heard you give, and I know you have always been considered an excellent speaker."

"Well, son, through my strength in the Lord, I have regenerated my spirit and I am determined to do all the good I can in this world during the few years I have remaining in my life. The service we render to mankind is the rent we pay for the space we occupy on earth."

Strangers on a train or on a bus would tell Mama of their troubles and she would listen and comfort them. We never did know how many people she met just once, who continued to write her, but we knew that she had a long list of correspondents whom she said needed her help

The most compelling force in Mama's life was the desire to help others. She sincerely loved all mankind and wished to help those in need. In the final analysis she felt her sorrows were insignificant compared with the sorrows of those about her. She lived by doing good for others. She regenerated her own spirit as she put into action her love for all people.

EPILOGUE

One Sunday evening just after I retired I was awakened by an urgent phone call from a friend in Tulare. The message was, "Your mother had a serious stroke and is in the hospital. Come at once."

I wired my sisters—Little Sis in New York, Big Sis in Salem, Oregon, and Bunny in Portland, and hurried the two hundred miles to Tulare.

Mama was unconscious. I could not see the doctor so I called on the friend who had phoned me.

Mama had just returned from a meeting in Exeter twenty miles away with a carload of young people. Although she was seventy years old, she was still taking young people on these trips and enjoying them tremendously. As she delivered the last of the young people to his home, she went into the house to speak to the mother who was a good friend and neighbor. She was invited in to have a cup of coffee and as she sat down she pitched forward and lost consciousness.

I thought afterwards how fortunate it was that she did not have the stroke while she was driving the carload of young people. I wondered if people with the determination and energy of Mama could stave off a stroke until they had delivered those they loved to safety.

Little Sis wired that she was unable to come to Mama, but Big Sis, Bunny and I stood by her bedside that afternoon as she remained unconscious. She did not speak, but through extra-sensory perception she knew we were there. One eyelid fluttered and she held out her hand. I clasped her loving hand in mine and soon passed it along to Big Sis for I felt Mama was groping for another. Big Sis, in turn, passed her hand along to Bunny and then Mama groped for Little Sis's hand. I tried to tell her that Little Sis was unable to come because of illness, but we couldn't tell whether she understood. Perhaps she missed her baby most of all.

Here we three grown people stood by Mama's bed expecting to offer her comfort, but she, out of her great love and in her unconscious state, was offering love and comfort to us.

We recalled our childhood days and the many happy times we had together. As adults we knew we had often been miserably poor when we were small children, but we never missed material things for Mama gave us love and fostered an eagerness for life. As children we were unaware that our family was poor since Mama provided delicious nourishing food and our mealtimes were happy occasions.

True, she was forever sewing, lengthening garments, turning them so that the worn side was inside and not evident. Sometimes she got outgrown garments from our relatives and fixed them so that they appeared brand new, refitting and rebuilding according to our measurements. She built in us a pride for our clothes and none of us as children ever had a feeling of inferiority. We were so loved and so happy that we were unaware that we were poor.

The doctor said that Mama might possibly live. There was just a small chance. He further said that if she did live, she undoubtedly would be bedridden all the rest of her life.

Our prayers were only that God's will would be done. Two days later, she passed away in her sleep.

Friends and neighbors streamed to the front door of the old family home to tell us of their love for Mama and all the wonderful kindly things she had done for them.

Hundreds of people paid tribute to her great love for all humanity.

So great was Mama's love that each of us felt she loved us the most. She seemed to have the capacity to make each one feel that he had a special place in her heart.

As we put away Mama's effects, we found in her Bible, which Papa had given her for Christmas in 1927, this poem by Eleanor Northrop Keys.

To My Husband

These children of our youthful love have twined
Themselves in my heart. Oh, they may find
The best in life—full strength and beauty—grace
Of soul and mind—but you, you have first place.
Together we have met the blows, the care;
At pain we have smiled, and laughed when life was fair
In time to come they'll go their separate ways,
And I shall love as ever, watch and praise
But not intrude, because they are apart,
Their lives their own—but you, you hold my heart.

THE END